Scholastic Literacy Skills

Grammar and punctuation

AGES 5–7

PHOTOCOPIABLE SKILLS ACTIVITIES

Author	Leonie Bennett	Designer	Rachael Hammond
Editor	Roanne Davis	Illustrations	Frasier Worth
Assistant editor	Dulcie Booth	Cover artwork	Gerald Hawksley
Series designer	Lynda Murray	Scottish consultant	Margaret Scott

Published by Scholastic Ltd
Villiers House
Clarendon Avenue
Leamington Spa
Warwickshire CV32 5PR

Text © Leonie Bennett 2001
© 2001 Scholastic Ltd

Printed by Ebenezer Baylis & Son Ltd, Worcester

1 2 3 4 5 6 7 8 9 0   1 2 3 4 5 6 7 8 9 0

British Library Cataloguing-in-Publication Data
A catalogue record for this book is available from the British Library.

ISBN 0-439-01949-4

Acknowledgments

The publishers would like to thank the following for permission to reproduce copyright material.
Spike Milligan Productions Ltd for the use of one verse from 'If' from *Unspun socks from a chicken's laundry* © 1981, Spike Milligan (1981, MJ Hobbs and Michael Joseph).
Mirror Group Newspapers for the use of 'Moods' by Robert Whitson and 'Snow' by Peter Bradley from a poetry competition which appeared in the *Daily Mirror* © 1976, The Mirror (1976, Mirror Group Newspapers).

Thank you also to **Elaine Hampton and Karen Leigh**, experienced Key Stage 1 teachers, for their valuable input during the development of this book.

Every effort has been made to trace copyright holders and the publishers apologise for any inadvertent omissions.

Contents

Introduction

Welcome to grammar and punctuation

The *Scholastic Literacy Skills: Grammar and punctuation series* equips teachers with resources and subject training enabling them to teach grammar and punctuation throughout the primary years. The focus of the series is on sentence-level work, so called because grammar and punctuation primarily involve the construction and understanding of sentences. Many teachers approach the teaching of grammar with memories of it as the driest subject. They may wonder how they can make it interesting for their own class.

The *Scholastic Literacy Skills: Grammar and punctuation series* works from the premise that grammar can be interesting and creative if it is embedded in activities that experiment with language and investigate the use of language in real contexts. Throughout, children are encouraged to explore the ways in which grammar and punctuation structure our day-to-day conversation, writing and reading and help us to communicate our thoughts and ideas.

The series is based upon several principles about the teaching of grammar:

Meaningful sentence-level work

Children's attention is drawn to the *purposes* of the texts on which the activities are based. The series does contain exercises in which sentences have been constructed purely to provide examples of a particular feature, however, this is complemented by work based on poems or fiction extracts which can be enjoyed for their own sake. There are also examples of other genres, including notices, labels, instructions and recounts. The aim is consistently to refer children to genuine texts. They are encouraged to look for examples of sentence-level features in the environment, in their own work and in other texts at home and in the classroom. There are frequent opportunities for children to continue writing in the same genre.

Structure is essential

While the *Scholastic Literacy Skills: Grammar and punctuation* series is full of lively material, it is underpinned by a clear and deliberate structure. Teaching sentence-level aspects of English effectively demands a structured approach that uses common sense and introduces features such as sentence structure and punctuation in ways that build continuity and progression into children's learning.

Active enjoyment

This is not a book of basic drills. The activities in the series are constructed in a way that involves a lot of active investigative work and play with language. The underlying premise is that language is interesting, that understanding it can be fascinating and working with it can be fun.

Working with *Scholastic Literacy Skills: Grammar and punctuation Ages 5–7*

Structure of this book

The skills work is delivered in the form of teacher-mediated photocopiable sheets accompanied by teacher's notes.

The material is divided into two main sections: Ages 5–6 and Ages 6–7. There are further subdivisions into units, each of which deals with a particular aspect of sentence-level work. There are some features included, such as adjectives, that are not specified in the National Literacy Strategy (NLS) for England, but which most teachers agree it is important to begin exploring before Key Stage 2/Primary 4.

The number of activities in each unit varies according to the aspect of grammar or punctuation under consideration. Some sentence-level work requires more frequent revisiting (as is evidenced by the term-by-term repetition of some objectives in the NLS framework). *Scholastic Literacy Skills: Grammar and punctuation Ages 5–7* reflects this requirement – objectives are returned to and activity types repeated – to ensure that skills are revised and reinforced.

The photocopiable pages in each unit are prefaced by introductory teacher's notes under the following headings:

Objectives   The learning objectives for the unit.

Ways of teaching   Background information that might be useful in teaching the subject matter of the unit, together with suggestions of how to introduce the grammar feature or punctuation point. This often includes ideas for activities to be undertaken during shared reading or writing.

About the activities   An explanation of each photocopiable page and ways of supporting the children carrying it out. References to the use of the photocopiable poster texts and progression within the activities are also given. Sometimes a shared introductory activity is suggested to prepare the children for the work. Extensions or continuations are also often proposed.

Following up   Optional activity suggestions to develop the content of the unit. These often include further class as well as individual activities.

Differentiation

The *Scholastic Literacy Skills: Grammar and punctuation* series is designed to be flexible, to be used according to the needs of individual children. The activities within each unit are presented in order of difficulty, beginning with the simplest tasks. You can therefore allocate them to the children according to their skill levels.

Many of the grammar and punctuation points are revised in series of pages that offer progressively more challenging versions of the same activity. These are indicated as (1), (2) and so on, where (1) is the easiest task, (2) is more difficult. Children of average ability can work their way through these from first to last, while more able children can begin with one of the later pages and go on to one of the follow-up tasks. Frequently, there are 'continuation' tasks suggested, where the children are asked to carry on with a story or write a further verse for a poem. Such tasks could be allocated to higher ability children only. Children of lower ability may work on the simpler pages only, or on a reduced amount of material. If an activity asks them to carry out a certain number of tasks (for example, to complete eight sentences) you may wish to reduce the number of tasks required.

Although the material is divided into sections for 5–6 and 6–7 year-olds, it will often be appropriate for children in either age group to be allocated activities from the earlier or later section.

Posters for ages 5–6

There is enormous variation in reading ability in the first year of primary school and the author, therefore, cannot make assumptions about the sight vocabulary of the children attempting the early activities in this book. To help overcome this difficulty, three posters are provided for children aged 5–6, each of which carries a simple, rhyming text. These texts, along with the NLS Reception sight recognition list, provide the vocabulary on which many of the simplest activities are based.

Vocabulary is kept simple throughout the programme. Other activities for 5–6 year-olds use the sight recognition lists from the NLS for Years 1 and 2 in England together with a limited number of other common nouns.

It is suggested that, before tackling the relevant activity, you share the rhyming text (on the enlarged poster) with the children. In this way, you can be sure that the children are familiar with the vocabulary. There are also suggestions for shared writing and follow-up work that involves the children innovating from the poster text or using it as a model for their own independent writing.

Posters for ages 6–7

There are three photocopiable posters for 6–7 year-olds, each of which illustrates an important grammar and punctuation feature: capitalisation; verb tenses and speech marks. These posters can be enlarged and displayed as reminders to the children when they are engaged in their own writing.

A 'resource' not a 'scheme'

The photocopiable pages are a support for teaching. Those for 5–6 year-olds have brief activity notes for an adult helper at the bottom of each sheet. Those for 6–7 year-olds have notes for the children. However, successful teaching of the learning objectives can only be achieved by the class working in conjunction with the teacher. Photocopiable pages are intended to support, not replace, your explanation and discussion of the language issues.

Scholastic Literacy Skills: Grammar and punctuation series is not a scheme that children work their way through from beginning to end. It is a flexible teaching resource. The charts on pages 190–2 correlate individual activities with NLS sentence-level objectives and Scottish National Guidelines for English Language 5–14. These charts will enable you to select the activities that best support your planning. The notes at the start of every unit will further help you to choose activities from the photocopiable pages or from the follow-up sections that will meet the needs of your children.

My nan

This boy had a dog.

That boy had a rat.

My nan had a kangaroo.

What do you think of that?

This girl had a fish.

That girl had a cat.

My nan had an elephant.

What do you think of that?

Scholastic Literacy Skills
Grammar and punctuation

Put on your hat

It is cold.

Look at the snow.

Put on your hat.

Then we can go.

It is cold.

Look at the snow.

Put on your coat.

Then we can go.

I am hungry

Grandpa, I am hungry.
I want something to eat.

Do you want a sandwich?

No, I want a sweet.

Grandpa, I am hungry.
I want something to eat.

Do you want an apple?

No, I want a sweet.

Unit 1 Lower-case and capital letters

This unit aims to reinforce children's knowledge of the relationship between lower-case letters and their upper-case partners. Secure in this knowledge, the children will be able to go on to learn when to use capital letters, for example to start a sentence or a name or to indicate a title.

Contents
1.1 Match upper to lower case (1)
1.2 Match upper to lower case (2)
1.3 Lower-case letter snake
1.4 Upper-case letter cards

Objectives
- Reinforce the distinction between the lower-case and capital forms of each letter.
- Reinforce knowledge of alphabetical order.

Ways of teaching
It is important that children understand that capital letters have particular functions (like the ones that begin their names) and should not be mixed in with lower-case letters in their writing. During shared writing, emphasise the fact that you are using lower-case letters almost all of the time. When you do use a capital letter (for example, at the beginning of a sentence), point it out to the children as something special. They will probably also come across many occasions in stories where capital letters are used for emphasis: BOOM!

During shared reading, ask the children to point to a capital letter and find its lower-case version elsewhere on the page or pick it out from an alphabet of magnetic letters.

After shared writing, invite the children to circle all the capital letters in the text. Then invite them to help you to join with a line each capital to a matching lower-case letter.

Practise alphabetical ordering by covering up letters at random on an alphabet frieze. Recite the letters and ask the children to supply those that are missing.

About the activities

Activities 1.1 and 1.2
Match upper to lower case (1) and (2)
In activity 1.1, each butterfly should end up with both versions of two letters filled in – capitals on the top wings, lower case on the bottom wings.

Activity 1.2 provides further practice in matching capitals to lower-case letters, this time without the support of the alphabet on the page.

Activities 1.3 and 1.4
Lower-case letter snake and Upper-case letter cards
These pages are to be used together. You may wish to copy them onto card so that they can be reused. Activity sheet 1.4 should be cut up into individual letter cards beforehand and the children should collect the cards into a pack, in random order. They can then play games with them:
- Playing alone, they can match the capitals to their lower-case partners on the game board in activity 1.3.
- Playing with others, they can divide the alphabet between them and take it in turns to put down a letter in the correct place.

● Playing with others, the children can have a counter each and throw a dice to move along the snake on activity sheet 1.3. If the player holds the capital letter to match the lower-case letter that he or she lands on, that player can have another throw and move further along the board. The winner is the first one to reach z.

Following up Scatter an alphabet of magnetic capital letters onto the children's table and ask the children to position them in order, letter by letter. Then hand out the lower-case letters at random and ask the children to place each one below the appropriate capital. As they are doing this, ask the children to point out pairs of letters in which the capital is the same shape as the lower-case letter (c, k, o and so on).

Give pairs of children six upper- and lower-case letter pairs, randomly ordered. Who can sort their letters into the six pairs the quickest? Shuffle the sets of letters and hand them out between the children again to let them have another go.

Encourage the children to look carefully through some samples of their own writing to see if they can spot anywhere that they have mixed up capital letters with lower-case letters.

A B C...

A B C D E F G H I J K L M
N O P Q R S T U V W X Y Z
a b c d e f g h i j k l m n o p q r s t u v w x y z

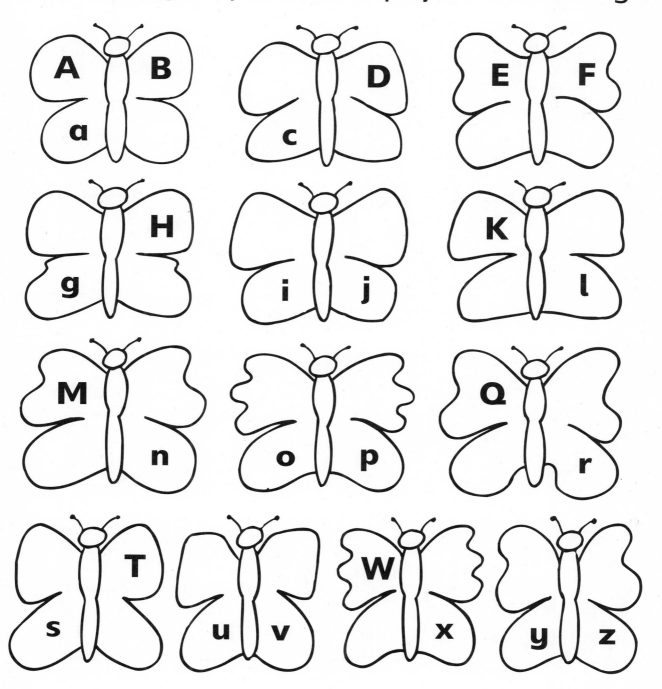

Fill in the empty butterfly wings with letter pairs. Use capital letters in the top wings and lower-case letters in the bottom wings.

Eggs

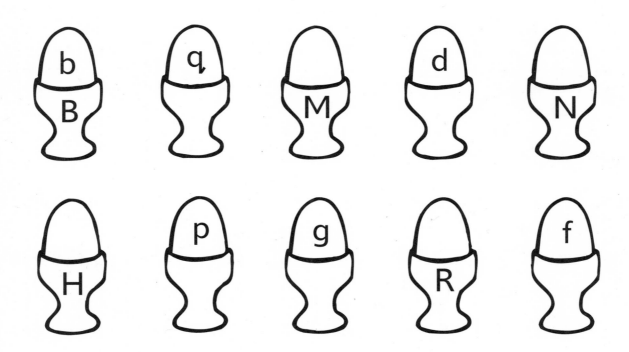

Match the lower-case letters to their upper-case partners. In the first part, join the eggs to the eggcups with a line. In the second part, fill in the missing letters.

Snakes alive!

a b c d e f g h i j k l m n o p q r s t u v w x y z

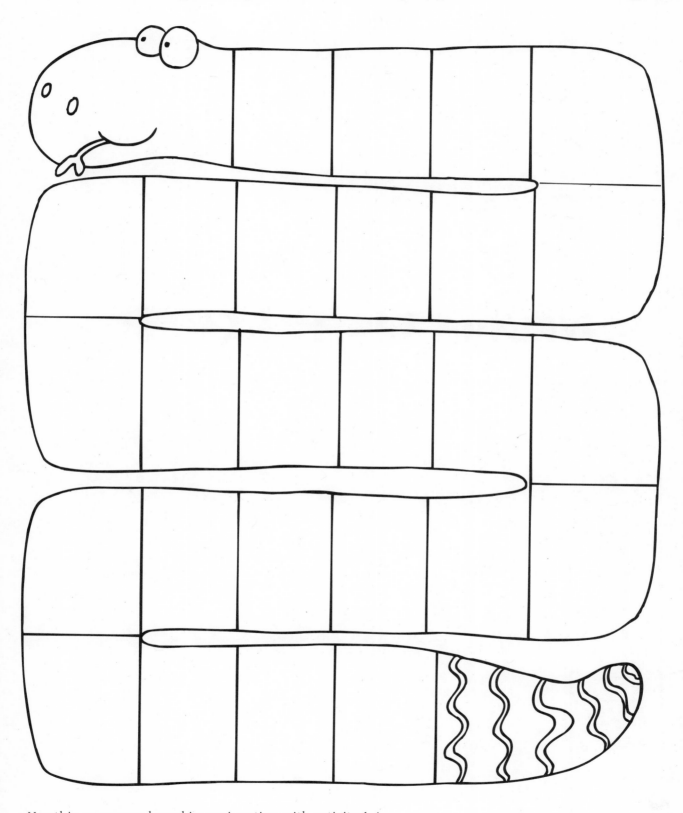

Use this as a game board in conjunction with activity 1.4.

Capital cards

A	B	C	D	E	F
G	H	I	J	K	L
M	N	O	P	Q	R
S	T	U	V	W	X
Y	Z				

Stick this sheet onto card and cut out the alphabet cards for use with activity 1.3.

Unit ② Capital letters, full stops and question marks

This unit focuses on the punctuation that indicates the beginnings and endings of sentences. A capital letter is not a punctuation mark, but its function in starting a sentence is taught at the same time as the full stop.

Children develop a growing awareness of sentences through their reading and writing. They often write sentences, but leave out the punctuation marks. These activities are intended to draw children's attention to the punctuation they need to include in their sentences. Reading aloud, taking account of punctuation that indicates pauses and changes of intonation, will help to demonstrate the purposes of punctuation.

Contents

Part 1
Capital letters and full stops
2.1 Capital letters and full stops (1)
2.2 Capital letters and full stops (2)
2.3 How many sentences? (1)
2.4 How many sentences? (2)
2.5 Picture story (1)
2.6 Picture story (2)
2.7 Leela's story

Part 2
Question marks and full stops
2.8 Find the question marks
2.9 Put in four full stops and four question marks
2.10 Put in the full stops and question marks (1)
2.11 Put in the full stops and question marks (2)

Part 1
Objectives

- Recognise that a sentence begins with a capital letter and ends with a full stop.
- Use capital letters and full stops to begin and end sentences.
- Understand that a line of writing is not necessarily the same as a sentence.

Ways of teaching

Ask the children what a sentence begins with. Look at sentences in Big Books and copy some out on the board. Help the children to see that all the sentences begin with a capital letter. Then ask what sentences end with, and help the children to find the full stops. Tell them that some sentences end with a question mark or an exclamation mark and show some examples, explaining that you will look at these more closely later.

Draw attention to capital letters and full stops regularly during shared reading and writing sessions, and in relation to the children's own writing. When reading, see if the children can notice what a full stop makes your voice do. Before you start any shared writing, ask the children what type of letter you need to use to begin the sentence.

Point out that a sentence is not the same as a line of writing. To emphasise this, write out a section of one of the poems from the posters, changing the line breaks. Show the children that the number of sentences has remained the same. As you are working through some shared writing, write each sentence with a different coloured pen.

About the activities

Activities 2.1 and 2.2

Capital letters and full stops (1) and **(2)**

Look at an enlarged version of Poster 1 and read through the poem with the children. Ask a child to come and point to the capital letter at the beginning of the first sentence. Another child can then point to the full stop at its end. Draw attention to the question marks at the end of lines 4 and 8, explaining that these also end sentences – special ones that ask questions.

Explain to the children that the poem has been written out incorrectly in activity 2.1 – there are no capital letters or full stops. Write a similar 'wrong' sentence on the board (for example, *my cat is ill*). Ask what is wrong with the first word and invite a child to change the initial *m* into a capital. Ask another child what is wrong with the end of the sentence and to add the full stop. Tell them to correct the sentences in activity 2.1 by sticking the capital letters over the appropriate lower-case letters and then adding full stops.

In activity 2.2, a variety of sentences have been written without capital letters or full stops. The children need to complete the activity with the same process as for 2.1.

Referring to Poster 1 and activity 2.1, ask the children to think what other animal Nan might have had and to write their own versions of the last two sentences: *My nan had a _____. What do you think of that?* More able children could think of more animals and make up additional verses.

Activities 2.3 and 2.4

How many sentences? (1) and **(2)**

Remind the children that sentences begin with a capital letter and end with a full stop and that a sentence is *not* the same as a line of writing. Using activity 2.3, ask them to read what the characters say and circle the capital letters and full stops. They should then count how many sentences there are in each speech bubble and write the number on the line. Finally, encourage them to imagine what Grandma is saying at the bottom of the page and write two sentences of their own.

Tell the children to read each story in activity 2.4 and then complete the page as for 2.3, writing their own sentences about swimming.

Activities 2.5 and 2.6

Picture story (1) and **(2)**

Read through each story with the children and point out how the pictures tell the stories. Tell the children to read the words carefully and decide where the sentences begin and end. Activity 2.5 has three sentences. 2.6 has four. The children should put in the three or four capital letters and the same number of full stops and then rewrite one complete sentence next to each picture.

Activity 2.7

Leela's story

Remind the children of the text on Poster 2 with the little fox and his mother getting ready to go out in the snow. Then enlarge activity 2.7 and read through the story extracts about Leela. Ask the children to tell you where they think you should pause as you re-read each paragraph. Invite individuals to write the capital letter and full stop where each sentence begins and ends. Let the children predict what happens next and write two or three sentences about it.

More able children can work in pairs with their own copy of the activity. They should read through each passage aloud, then note the number of sentences. If there are different answers, talk about them with the children.

Following up   Remove the capital letters and full stops from part of a text with which the children are familiar. Ask pairs or groups to put back them back. Compare and discuss different versions of the reconstituted text. Ask the children to find and read out sentences from other books in the classroom.

Encourage the children to read their own writing aloud, perhaps additional verses to 'Put on your hat' on Poster 2, thinking where they would naturally pause – to get a feel for where sentences begin and end.

**Part 2
Objectives**

- Recognise the question mark at the end of a sentence.
- Know when to use a question mark.
- Recognise the difference between a statement and a question.

Ways of teaching   Ask several children a question, such as How old are you? Do you like chocolate? Point out the fact that you are asking questions. Then tell the children to ask each other a question. Write some of their questions on the board, drawing attention to the question marks and why they are there. Ask individual children to copy over the question marks in a different-colour.

Display Posters 1 and 3 and ask the children which of the sentences are questions. Then ask a child to come up and point to the question mark at the end of each one. Can the children tell you why the other sentences don't have question marks? Make clear that there are two different kinds of sentences: those that tell us something and others that ask questions.

Point out how our voices change when we ask a question. Read out a few questions and statements, emphasising the differing intonation.

About the activities

Activity 2.8   **Find the question marks**
Explain that on this page, lots of people are asking Simon questions. Some of the sentences are the questions; the other sentences are his answers. The children need to decide which are which – circling the question marks. In pairs, they can then go on to practise asking and answering the questions, paying attention as they speak and listen to the differences in intonation (see 'Following up').

Activity 2.9   **Put in four full stops and four question marks**
Tell the children that none of the sentences on the sheet are finished and that you want them to complete them with the appropriate punctuation. Advise the children that, as they use each punctuation mark, they can cross it off at the bottom of the page.

Activities 2.10 and 2.11   **Put in the full stops and question marks (1) and (2)**
The children should finish these statements and questions by adding the appropriate punctuation. As an extension, they can give their own final question to a partner who should imagine they are the little fox in activity 2.10 or the girl in activity 2.11 and write an answer, remembering to write a sentence with a capital letter and full stop.

Following up In shared writing, create a new verse for the poem on Poster 3 by substituting a different type of food in line 3. Discuss with the children what kind of food you should eat if you are hungry. Make up a list of questions that Grandpa could ask.

Hide a familiar object in a bag and play a guessing game. Invite the children to ask you questions in order to find out what the object is, for example *What is it made of*? *How big is it*? *What colour is it*? *What does it feel like*? *Is it heavy*? *What is it used for*? Write the children's questions on the board, emphasising the question marks.

Choose a familiar character from a fairy tale such as 'Sleeping Beauty' or 'Little Red Riding Hood'. Adopt the role of that character and tell the children that they should ask you questions to find out who you are. They could ask, for example, *Did you eat porridge*? and *Are you a handsome young man*? Alternatively, ask a pair of children to agree on a character to 'be', and you, in co-operation with the rest of the children, can ask them questions. Encourage the children to word their questions carefully.

Ask the children to read aloud the questions and answers from activities 2.8, 2.10 and 2.11. Encourage them to change their intonation according to whether they are reading a question or a statement. Their voices should become higher at the end of a question. Practise reading other texts aloud, focusing on how the grammar and punctuation give clues to how it should be read, for example to pause slightly at commas and observe a longer pause after a full stop.

This and that

this boy had a dog

that boy had a rat

my nan had a kangaroo

what do you think of that?

this girl had a fish

that girl had a cat

my nan had an elephant

what do you think of that?

These sentences have no capital letters or full stops. Cut out the capital letters and stick them in the right places. Put in the full stops. Remember: a sentence doesn't need a full stop if it has a question mark.

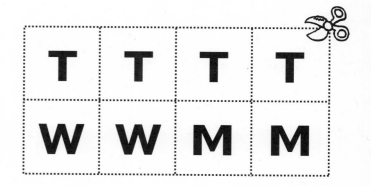

| T | T | T | T |
| W | W | M | M |

A fine fish

i am hungry

this is my sandwich

look at this fish

put on your boots

i want something to eat

we went swimming

i can see you

we can play in the park

P	I	W	I
L	T	I	W

These sentences have no capital letters or full
stops. Cut out the capital letters and stick
them in the right places. Put in the full stops.

Grandma

Put on your coat. Then we can go.

I am hungry. I want something to eat.

There are _____ sentences.   There are _____ sentences.

I want my mum. She is at home. I want to go home.

Come and play. We can go to my house. You can see my dog. She is called Bingo.

There are _____ sentences.   There are _____ sentences.

What is Grandma saying?

_____

_____

_____

Put rings around the capital letters and full stops in each bubble. How many sentences are there in each? Write two sentences of speech for Grandma.

New shoes

Raj went out with Mum. He got
some new shoes. Then he went
to see his gran. He showed her
his new shoes. She liked them.

There are _____
sentences.

It was very cold. Sally and Josh
went out. They played in Sally's
garden. Then they went to
Josh's house. His dad made them
hot chocolate. They sat by the
fire. Soon they were warm.

There are _____
sentences.

Sam can't swim. He goes to lessons.
He likes to play in the water. His
little sister can swim. His big brother
can swim. Sam doesn't like
swimming.

There are _____
sentences.

Do you like swimming?

_____

_____

_____

Put rings around the capital letters and full stops in each section. How many sentences are there
in each? Write two sentences about going swimming.

SCHOLASTIC photocopiable

See-saw

tom went on the
see-saw he fell
off he hurt his arm

Read the story. Put in the capital letters and full stops. Write one sentence next to each picture.

In the mud

I went to the park my
dog went too she went
in the mud dad was cross

_____

_____

_____

_____

_____

_____

_____

_____

Read the story. Put in the capital letters and full stops. Write one sentence next to each picture.

Leela

it was cold Leela wanted
to go out her mother
gave her a hat she put
it on

There are _____ sentences.

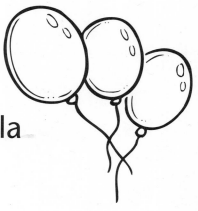

Leela went
out she saw three
balloons she wanted one Leela
ran after them her mum
ran after her

There are _____ sentences.

What do you think happened next?

_____

_____

_____

_____

Read the passage aloud. Where do you pause? Write in the capital letters and full stops, then count
the sentences. Write two or three sentences of your own about what happens next.

Questions

Are you cold?

Your book is
on the table.

What is that?

Yes, I can play.

That is Paula's dad.

Can you play?

It is a hat.

Can you see my book?

No, I am not cold.

Is that your dad?

How many questions are there? _____

Circle the question marks and count the questions. Cut out all the sentences and stick them down in pairs, matching questions and answers.

Fish and cats and dogs

That girl had a fish

I like the black cat

PURRR

I am at home

Do you want a sweet

What day is it

Is Dad at home

Is that his dog

I want a sandwich

.   .   .   .   ?   ?   ?   ?

Add the four full stops and four questions marks in the correct places.

Look at the snow

Look at the snow

I want to play

Can I put on this hat

Do you want to play

I am cold

Put on your boots

I want to go out

How many questions are there? _____

Q_____

_____

A_____

_____

Which of these sentences are questions? Which are 'telling' sentences? Add question marks and full stops. Write a question to ask the little fox and ask a friend to write an answer.

Asking or telling?

Was the dog in the snow

Was he cold

This is my house

Do you want a pizza

Look at this book

What do you want to do

Let's all go out to play

Do you want to go home

There are _____ questions.

Q _____

_____

A _____

_____

Which of these sentences are questions? Which are 'telling' sentences? Add full stops and question marks. Then write a question of your own and ask a friend to write an answer. Remind him or her to answer with a complete sentence.

Unit ③ Is it a sentence?

A sentence is a unit of language that makes sense on its own. It can be a statement or a question. In writing, a sentence begins with a capital letter and ends with a full stop, question mark or exclamation mark.

This unit looks at the features of a sentence and asks children to identify complete sentences and finish incomplete ones with words of their own and/or full stops.

It can take a long time and a lot of exposure before the notion of what constitutes a sentence is secure with many children. Their attention should be repeatedly drawn to the formation of sentences in shared and guided reading and writing.

In the context of their own writing, children should also be regularly reminded about what makes a sentence. Encourage them to apply what they learn in these units to the writing they are doing outside the programme.

Contents

3.1 Spot the sentences (1)
3.2 Spot the sentences (2)
3.3 Finish the sentences (1)

3.4 Finish the sentences (2)
3.5 Finish the questions (1)
3.6 Finish the questions (2)

Objectives

● Recognise a sentence.
● Understand that a sentence must make sense.
● Recognise the difference between a phrase and a sentence.
● Appreciate that a sentence can be a statement or a question.

Ways of teaching

Read Poster 1 with the children. Point to the first line and ask if it is a sentence. How can they tell? Remind the children of what they have already learned about sentences – that they begin with a capital letter and end with a full stop or question mark. Look at some other lines from the poem in the same way.

Now write an incomplete sentence on the board (for example, I *saw a*). Ask the children if this is a sentence. Does it begin with a capital letter and end with a full stop? It doesn't have both, so it isn't a sentence. If you add a full stop, does it become a sentence? Explain to the children that this group of words isn't a sentence because it doesn't make sense – there is something missing. Invite them to think of ways of making the words into a sentence, for example I *saw a dinosaur*.

About the activities

Activities 3.1 and 3.2

Spot the sentences (1) and **(2)**
Briefly remind the children of what they already know about sentences.

The children can work in pairs, reading each group of words and deciding whether or not it is a sentence and counting how many sentences there are. More able children can complete those that do not make sense by adding more words and a full stop.

In activity 3.2, help the children to turn the last phrase into a sentence by using one of the words provided, or a different one that they think of, and a full stop.

Activities 3.3 and 3.4

Finish the sentences (1) and **(2)**
You may wish to enlarge these pages for use as a class activity.

Read through each group of words in activity 3.3 and ask the children if it makes sense. If it does, what needs to be added to make it into a sentence? Invite a child to write the full stop in the right place. Then ask the children to look again at the other phrases. What words could they add to make them make sense?

The activity could be given to pairs of children to decide which groups of words just need a full stop. More able children should be able to complete the remaining sentences.

For activity 3.4, when they have successfully worked through the same procedure, ask the children to think of something they would like to write about one of the illustrations on the sheet. Tell them to write a full sentence on the back of the sheet.

Activities 3.5 and 3.6

Finish the questions (1) and **(2)**
All of these questions are incomplete in some way. Some just need a question mark. Others do not make sense and need additional words, either from the lists at the bottom of the pages or the children's own. You may wish to enlarge the pages for use as a class activity (as for 3.3 and 3.4) or the children can work on them in pairs.

Following up

Using a Big Book, cover up the last part of a sentence with a Post-it Note. Ask the children to suggest different ways of completing the sentence, then compare these with the original.

Invite the children to write a sentence about themselves and share it with a partner. Together, they can check their writing to see if each has written a sentence. Does it begin with a capital letter and end with a full stop? Does it make sense on its own? They could then work together to make up and write out a question to ask another pair.

Sentence check (1)

Yes ✓   No ✗

This is a big house.   ☐

Mum is   ☐

They went to the shop.   ☐

Look at the   ☐

That boy is going to school.   ☐

I want a cake.   ☐

My cat had kittens.   ☐

We went out.   ☐

How many sentences are there? _____

Which of these are sentences? Put a tick next to each one that is, and a cross next to each one that is not. Count up the ticks.

Sentence check (2)

Yes ☑ ✓   No ☐ ✗

I am six. ☐

You are ☐

Look at Dad. ☐

That girl had two balls. ☐

That boy had ☐

I can see a cat. ☐

Put the bag on the table. ☐

I am going to ☐

I am going to the _____

shop   park   zoo

Which of these are sentences? Tick those that are and put crosses next to those that are not.
Then complete the last sentence.

Rats and dogs

My grandpa is _____

Dad likes my rat _____

My nan had an elephant _____

I had a _____

We want to go _____

We all went to _____

Get in the _____

Look at the kangaroo _____

I like dogs _____

I don't like _____

None of these are correct sentences. Put full stops at the end of those that make sense as they are. Complete the others by adding more words and then a full stop.

We like ice cream

It is a _____

I am cold _____

I want a _____

I want something to eat _____

It is a red car _____

Look at the _____

We like ice cream _____

Put on your _____

We can go to _____

I like school _____

None of these are correct sentences. Put full stops at
the end of those that make sense as they are.
Complete the others by adding more words and then
a full stop. Then write a sentence about one of the pictures.

Make a question (1)

Is that Anna's book _____

Was he in the house _____

Can you _____

What do you want to do _____

Do you like _____

Is this Joe's ball _____

Was it a big car_____

Do you want a sweet _____

swim   hop   apples   ice cream

None of these questions is complete.
If they make sense, add question marks.
Finish each one that doesn't make sense
by adding more words and a question mark.

Make a question (2)

Are you cold _____

Do you want to see my _____

Is it a _____

Are you going to school _____

Do you want a _____

Can we go to the _____

Can I play with the cat _____

Is this your _____

book   **car**   **shop**   **park**   **pen**   **mug**

None of these questions is complete.
If they make sense, add question marks.
Finish each one that doesn't make sense
by adding more words and a question mark.

Unit 4 Sentences make sense

This unit reinforces the concept of a sentence, but focuses on the need for a sentence to make sense. Children begin by sorting out mixed-up sentences and go on to create a variety of sentences using wordbanks and then write sentences of their own. Attention is repeatedly drawn to a sentence as a group of words that makes sense on its own.

Contents

Part 1
Word order
4.1 Make the poem
4.2 Sort out the sentences (1)
4.3 Sort out the sentences (2)
4.4 Sort out the questions (1)
4.5 Sort out the questions (2)
4.6 Alien questions

Part 2
Making sentences
4.7 Make a sentence (1)
4.8 Make a sentence (2)
4.9 Make a sentence (3)
4.10 Make three sentences (1)
4.11 Make three sentences (2)
4.12 How many sentences can you make?
4.13 Picture story (1)
4.14 Picture story (2)
4.15 Make sentences – accidents
4.16 What happens in the morning?
4.17 Write about the picture

Objectives
● Understand that sentences must make sense.
● Reinforce awareness that a line of writing is not the same as a sentence.
● Recognise and complete incomplete sentences.
● Recognise sentences in their own writing.

Part 1
Ways of teaching

Remind the children of the features of a sentence then write out a *mixed-up* sentence (for example, *like I dog. my*) and an *incomplete* sentence (such as *I went to*). Discuss with the children why these are not sentences. Look for capital letters and full stops and then focus on the fact that they do not make sense – either the words are in the wrong order or something is missing. Together, work out how they can be rewritten to make them into sentences. Do the same with a mixed-up question, looking for the question mark to go at the end.

Choose a familiar sentence from your current Big Book. Display the words (and punctuation) on cards and invite children to come and arrange the cards into a sentence, including the full stop and capital letter.

About the activities

Activity 4.1

Make the poem
Tell the children that the lines on the sheet are made up from the lines of the poem on Poster 2. Ask them to cut out the words and move them around to try to make the sentences. They can then rewrite each line as a sentence and make the two verses of the poem.

Suggest to the children that they look first for the capital letter to start the sentence and then find the full stop or question mark to show them where the sentence ends. Remind them that each sentence must make sense.

Activities 4.2 and 4.3

Sort out the sentences (1) and **(2)**

These activities set similar tasks to 4.1 – the groups of words can be reordered to make sentences. The first two sentences of activity 4.3 are from the rhyme on Poster 1. All the other sets of words make up sentences that the children have not read before.

Ask them to rewrite each line as a sentence. It may help to cut out the words so that they can be moved about to make a sentence.

Ask the children what they should look for to start the sentence (a capital letter) and what they should look for to show them where the sentence ends (a full stop or question mark). Does each sentence make sense?

Activities 4.4 and 4.5

Sort out the questions (1) and **(2)**

Tell the children that the words in each set have been mixed up and you want them to sort each group into a question. Once again, ask them what they should look for to start the sentence (the capital letter) and, this time, what they should look for to end the question (the question mark).

In activity 4.5, those who are confident could be asked to think up their own short question (not more than five words long). It can be about anything, but if they struggle for ideas, you could give them possible openings, such as *Are you…* or *Can you…* Explain that they should write one word in each box. Ask them to check it with an adult, then cut it up and give the mixed-up words to a partner to sort out.

Activity 4.6

Alien questions

Introduce this activity by telling the children that an alien has just landed on Earth and that the children on the sheet are asking it questions that have got muddled. Ask the children to sort out the questions and write each one in the speech bubble. They should then think of a question that they would like to ask the alien. They could also draw a picture of themselves asking the question.

Following up

Children could make their own mixed-up sentences. Encourage them to look in books for a sentence to copy out and cut up into individual words. These words can then be given to others to sort into sentences. The same activity can be carried out with questions.

Ask the children to look carefully at their own writing and to identify complete sentences. Does each of their sentences make sense on its own?

Encourage the children to pay attention to full stops and capital letters when they are reading aloud. Guide them to seeing how the demarcation of sentences helps them to make better sense of what they read. Point out how you pause when you get to a full stop and how your voice goes higher at the end of a question.

**Part 2
Ways of teaching**

These activities further consolidate recognition of sentences and lead the children on to writing their own sentences with support.

Choose a sentence from a shared reading text and write the individual words onto large cards. Make a few extra cards to extend the number of sentences that can be made, plus a full stop card. For example, if your sentence is *Max went to school*, you might add the words *bed* and *Anna*. Use initial capital letters for words that can easily start a sentence. Let a group of children (one for each letter plus one for the full stop) each hold up a card and ask them to work out how to stand in order to make a sentence. Two people will be left out! Ask the rest of the class to suggest how the 'person or thing' words could move about to make different sentences.

About the activities

Activities 4.7 to 4.9

Make a sentence (1) to **(3)**
Advise the children that each group of words in these activities can be made into a correct sentence.

In activity 4.7, they should write the sentences out on the line underneath each time. Remind them to look for the capital letter and full stop to begin and end each sentence. They may like to go on to write a short sentence of their own that they cut up and give to a partner to rearrange.

In activity 4.8, tell the children to make a sentence using *some* of the words each time. They could draw a line to join up the words in order before writing the sentence on the line. A variety of sentences can be made and you may wish to talk through a few before letting the children have a go. Let them know that they do not need to use all the words. Point out that *the* is included twice in the bottom section. Talk about when *the* would have a capital letter.

For activity 4.9, nearly all of the capital letters have been left out, so the children will need to decide which words should begin their sentences.

Activities 4.10 and 4.11

Make three sentences (1) and **(2)**
Children should use the words in activity 4.10 to make three different sentences, each starting with *Look*. Remind them to use a full stop at the end of each sentence. In this activity and in 4.11, let the children know that they may use a word more than once.

In activity 4.11, ask the children to look carefully at the picture and write three sentences about what they can see, using the words provided. Point out that none of the words begins with a capital letter, but the children will have to use a capital letter to start each of their sentences. Ask them what they will use to end each sentence.

Activity 4.12

How many sentences can you make?
This time, the children are asked to make as many sentences as they can, using only the words provided. They could work in pairs, with one child as scribe. It may help them to cut out the words and move them around. Advise them to write down each sentence as soon as they have made it, as they may want to reuse some of the words in another sentence.

Activities 4.13 and 4.14

Picture story (1) and **(2)**
Talk with the children about what is happening in each picture. Point out that some vocabulary is provided, but, together, you may want to write up some more. The children may also need help if they wish to use the verbs (*covered*, *barked* and *fell*) in a different tense. However, this would be a good opportunity

to remind them that most stories are told as if they happened some time ago. In each activity, the children should write one sentence next to each picture to tell the whole story, and then add another sentence to continue it.

Activity 4.15   **Make sentences – accidents**
Discuss the action in the pictures and make sure that the children can read the words next to each one. Ask them to write a sentence next to each picture to describe what is happening. They can then write one or two sentences of their own about an accident that happened to them or to someone they know.

Activity 4.16   **What happens in the morning?**
Talk briefly about what the children do every school morning. You may want to write up some helpful words or phrases, such as *wake up, wash, get dressed, have breakfast*. Ask the children to write a sentence next to each picture that describes what they think the boy is doing. Then they can write a sentence of their own about something else *they* do to get ready for school.

Activity 4.17   **Write about the picture**
Explore what is happening in the picture and check that the children can read the words beneath it. Ask them to write about the picture, then about something that has happened when they have been shopping.

Following up   Cover up the text on the pages of a Big Book and, together, compose a sentence to go with the picture on each page. If appropriate to the children's abilities, go back and write a second sentence saying something further about each picture. Ask the children to tell you where to put the capital letter and full stop each time.

Provide a story starter, for example *Yesterday, in the supermarket, I saw a tiny man, no bigger than my little finger.* Tell the children that you would like them to carry on with the story. Go around the class, asking each child to contribute a complete sentence. It doesn't matter if the story gets silly – the focus is on making single sentences.

Write a collaborative story and ask children to identify sentences as you scribe. Ask them to tell you where to put capital letters and full stops. Invite children to read out what you have written, paying attention to the punctuation in their delivery. Encourage them to see how pausing at the full stops helps to make the meaning clear.

Put on your hat

is	It	cold.	
at	snow.	Look	the
on	hat.	your	Put
go.	Then	can	we

cold.	It	is	
at	Look	snow.	the
coat.	Put	on	your
can	Then	go.	we

Cut out the words from each set. Then stick them down to make sentences from the poem 'Put on your hat' on Poster 2.

Rats, cats and dogs

Cut out the words from each line. Make each line into a sentence. Look for the capital letter and full stop.

rat.	boy	had	That	a
had	fish.	This	girl	a
big.	My	is	dog	
like	cats.	I		
at	Look	rat.	the	
swimming.	We	go	can	

I want...

Cut out the words from each line. Make each line into a sentence. Look for the capital letter and full stop.

hungry.	am	I	
want	sweet.	a	I
went	Grandpa	home.	
old.	dog	is	
want	I	ice cream.	My
Mum	at	is	an
			home.

Questions (1)

Cut out each line of words and stick them down in a sentence. Look for the capital letter and question mark.

is	What	that?		
come	Can	and	you	play?
this	Is	car?	my	
a	bike?	Do	want	you
you	Do	my	bike?	like
it	Is	cold!		

Questions (2)

want	Do	you	apple?	an
book?	this	Is	my	
you	help	Can	me?	
box?	What	in	is	the
to	you	Are	going	school?
you	swim?	Can		

Cut out each group of words. Stick them down in sentences. Look for the capital letters and question marks to help you. Then write your own question in the empty box. Cut out the words and mix them up. Give them to a friend to sort out.

Hello, Alien!

name?   Is   your   What

want?   do   What   you

are   from?   you   Where

Make each group of words into a question. Write each question in a speech bubble. What would *you* ask the alien? Write your question in the bottom bubble.

My cat

cat. This
my is

_____

my I
like mum.

_____

big was
a It dog.

_____

see She
cat. a can

_____

sister is
My two.

_____

Make each group of words into a sentence. Look for the capital to begin it and the full stop to end it.

Pets

dog

I

big

a

cat

saw

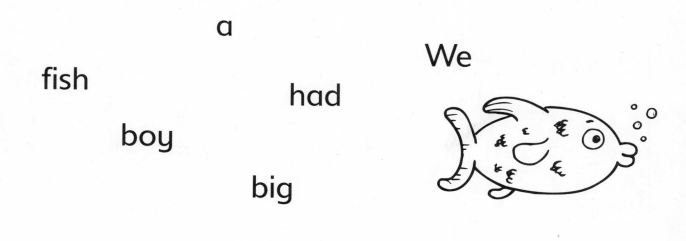

a

We

fish

had

boy

big

rat

the

car

went

Dad

The

in

Make a sentence from each group of words. You don't have to use all of them. Remember to look for the capital letter and add a full stop.

Name

The blue car

new

look

blue

for

the

box

at

car

---

would

put

like

put

I

hat

hat

my

boots

to

---

to

at

go

night

can't

we

the

Monday

park

Make a sentence from each group of words. You don't have to use all of them. You will need to use a capital letter and a full stop each time.

Look!

at   bed   for

my   girl

the   .

monster

1. Look _____

2. Look _____

3. Look _____

Make three different sentences beginning with *Look*, using the words provided. Don't forget to use the full stop.

The park

dogs   a   we   park
        the   saw   went
to   swan   three   .

1. _____

2. _____

3. _____

Make up three different sentences about the picture, using the words provided. Remember to use the full stop.

Our day out

park   and   Mum   to

the   .   shop

out   went   I

_____

_____

_____

_____

_____

_____

How many different sentences can you make with these words? You can use each word more than once.

On the beach

_____

_____

asleep   beach

_____

_____

covered   sand

_____

_____

sand   pies

What happened next?

Write a sentence next to each picture to tell the story. Use the back of this sheet to write about what happened next and draw a picture to go with your sentence.

Clowning about

_____

_____

clown   bike

_____

_____

dog   barked

_____

_____

fell   clown

_____

_____

dog   bike

What do you think might happen next?

_____

Write a sentence next to each picture to tell the story. Write a sentence to say what happened next.

Oops!

doll   dropped   pond

fell   boy   scooter

let   go   kite

What else happened?

Write a sentence next to each picture, saying what happened. Then write one or two sentences about an accident that you or a friend had.

Before school

_____

_____

_____

_____

_____

_____

_____

_____

_____

Before school I _____

_____

Write a sentence next to each picture, saying what the boy does in the morning. Then write a sentence about something _you_ do before you go to school.

Shopping

shopping   boot   baby   car
barking   trolley   crying   dog

1. _____

_____

2. _____

_____

3. _____

_____

Write three sentences about what is happening in the picture. Then write a sentence about a time when you went shopping.

Unit ⑤ Signs and sentences

This unit focuses on sentences in different genres – recounts and notices. The first two activities look at short captions that can be used to sum up a picture. The remaining ones look at notices and signs in the school environment. The idea of what makes a sentence is constantly reinforced as children are asked to decide whether or not a particular group of words is a sentence. The aim of this unit is to look at different types of sentences and use them as models for the children's own writing.

Contents

5.1 Captions (1) **5.4** Notices in school (2)
5.2 Captions (2) **5.5** Notices in school (3)
5.3 Notices in school (1)

Objectives

● Identify sentences.
● Write simple sentences in a variety of genres.
● Recognise if simple sentences make sense.

Ways of teaching

Draw the children's attention to the many examples of writing around them in the classroom. Probably, there will be lots of different types of writing – labels, instructions, explanations, recounts and so on. You may want to introduce the idea of labels for signs that just tell you the names of things, but otherwise, focus on whether or not the texts in them are sentences. Can the children tell you which are and which are not? Encourage them to test them out. For each one, ask: *Does it begin with a capital letter and end with a full stop or a question mark? Does it make sense alone?* Write on the board, incorrectly, a selection of the sentences you have identified, then invite children to tell you where to put the capital letter and the full stop.

Ask the children to suggest signs and notices you could put up in the classroom. Are there some things that everyone has to do or remember? For example, *Wash your hands before lunch* or *Only two people allowed in the listening corner.* Talk about how to word them (simply) and how to write them out (clearly).

About the activities

Activities 5.1 and 5.2

Captions (1) and (2)
Talk through the pictures and sentences with the children on the first sheet. Then read out the sentences, explaining that each one matches one of the first three pictures. Ask the children to join the sentence to its picture with a line and then write a sentence of their own to go with the last picture.

You may want to practise composing simple sentences to caption pictures during shared writing. With the children's help, compose a sentence that 'sums up' a photograph or an illustration in a picture book.

In activity 5.2, the capital letters and full stops have been left out. Talk through the pictures and sentences as before. Then tell the children to write each sentence next to the appropriate picture and make up their own sentence for the last one.

Activities 5.3

Notices in school (1)

Revise the different kinds of writing displayed on the walls of the classroom or elsewhere in the school (see 'Ways of teaching'). Tell them that the texts in the activity came from one classroom and check that they know what each one says. Remind them that a sentence can end in a full stop or a question mark. Encourage them then to find two signs on display in their classroom (or elsewhere in the school) and write the text in the empty boxes, giving them ticks if they are sentences and crosses if they are not.

Activities 5.4 and 5.5

Notices in school (2) and (3)

Ask the children if there are any notices in your classroom or school that are sentences telling people to do something, or not to do something – instructions. You might like to invite the children to be sentence detectives and go and hunt for some. Talk about the fact that signs often have pictures as well as words. Why do the children think that is? (To make the meaning clearer, so people will notice them and so on.) What are these pictures usually like? (Very simple, showing only what is important.) If there aren't any suitable instances of illustrated notices in your school, show some examples or sketch out a few on the board, such as a sign saying *Take off your muddy shoes*, showing a pair of dirty shoes with a cross through them, or *Please wait here*, showing someone sitting on a chair.

Explain that the notices in activities 5.4 and 5.5 tell people to do (or not to do) something. However, there is something wrong with all of the sentences and the children need to complete or rewrite them so that they make sense, begin with a capital letter and end with a full stop.

Look at the texts on the notices in activity 5.4. Why aren't they sentences? (Because they don't make sense – a word is missing from each.) Tell the children to complete each one with one of the words given. Also discuss the fact that only two of them have an illustration. What do they think could be drawn on the other notices that would help to make it clear what they are about?

Ask the children why the sentences in activity 5.5 are not sentences. (Because they are muddled and therefore don't make sense.) The children should sort them out and write the correct sentence under each picture. Talk about the last picture and ask the children what they think it is saying. Encourage them to think of a sentence of their own to write underneath. They can then draw suitable pictures in the three notices that are not illustrated. Remind them to draw something very simple and not to put anything in the picture that isn't mentioned in the sentence.

Following up

Children could work in pairs to think of and design a new sign for your classroom. It could tell people about something, tell them something they should do or ask them a question (for example, *Do you like our models*?). When the children have made up a sentence they can write it on a large sheet of paper, not forgetting to use a capital letter and a full stop or question mark.

Suggest that the children design and make signs or notices that they would like to put up at home – perhaps in their bedroom or on the outside of their bedroom door.

A nice day out?

It rained.

We had ice cream.

We went to the park.

_____

_____

_____

Join each sentence to one of the first three pictures with a line. Write a sentence to describe what happens in the last picture.

Monkey business

we all went on the bus

i liked the monkeys

kim got all muddy

Write each sentence under the correct picture, adding the capital letter and full stop. What happened in the last picture? Write your own sentence for it.

In the classroom

Class 2 ☐

Billy ☐

Lisa ☐

What day is it today? ☐

It is sunny today. ☐

Put your lunch box here. ☐

☐

☐

Tick the signs that are sentences. Put a cross by those that are not. Find two signs on the wall in school and write them in the boxes. Are they sentences?

Clean and tidy

Please _____
away the paints.

Wash your
_____.

Please hang
_____ your coat.

Keep _____
bookshelf tidy.

up   the   put   hands

Use a word from the bottom of the page to complete each sentence. Draw pictures in the empty boxes to show what the notices are for.

Signs

run. do not
Please

the away. Put
brushes

our to school.
Welcome

Write each group of words as a correct sentence. Then write a sentence to go with the last picture.
Draw pictures to illustrate the first two sentences.

Unit ⑥ Grammatical awareness

Most school-age children demonstrate grammatical awareness every time they speak. They do not need to be able to identify nouns and verbs in order to use them. They understand how to put different parts of speech together in order to make meaning. It is this understanding that they use during literacy activities when they check that what they are reading or writing 'sounds right'.

The activities in this unit ask children to choose the appropriate word to complete sentences. In most of the activities, children will need to select the word that sounds right from a bank of different parts of speech.

Contents
6.1 Which words fit? (1)
6.2 Which words fit? (2)
6.3 Which words fit? (3)
6.4 What did they say? (1)

6.5 What did they say? (2)
6.6 Make two new sentences (1)
6.7 Make two new sentences (2)
6.8 Finish the story

Objectives
- Expect text to make sense.
- Substitute appropriate words if a text doesn't make sense.
- Use awareness of grammar to work out the meanings of new or unfamiliar words.
- Investigate the sorts of words that 'fit' in a text.

Ways of teaching
Emphasise to the children how important it is that the text they are reading makes sense. In shared reading, read a sentence, deliberately including a mistake as you read, then ask if it made sense. What word do the children think would make sense there?

Cover a word in a Big Book with a Post-it Note. Take suggestions from the children as to what word might be hidden. Try out some of the alternatives to the original and talk about the sorts of words that would fit and those that wouldn't.

Write out a sentence with a gap, for example *We _____ into the old house.* Read it through and ask the children what is wrong with it. Most will be able to tell you that something is missing. Remind them that sentences must make sense and that only certain sorts of words will make sense in this space. Ask whether *big* or *brown* would fit. What about *bike* or *dinosaur*? Ask what words would fit – *went, walked, ran* and so on. At this stage, it isn't necessary to tell the children that these words are verbs.

About the activities

Activities 6.1 to 6.3

Which words fit? (1) to **(3)**

The sentences in activity 6.1 will all be familiar to the children from the posters. Explain that each missing word is one of three in the box underneath. They should try out each of the words to see which one sounds right, then write it in the space.

The sentences in activity 6.2 will be familiar in their sentence structure and vocabulary, but this time, the children need to select the right word from a wider choice of words. Again, encourage the children to try out each word that they think might fit to see if it sounds right in the sentence.

Activity 6.3 is similar to 6.2, but will suit more able children. There are two gaps in each sentence and the vocabulary is more challenging. Point out to the children that some of the words will fit more than one space, so they will need to read the sentences carefully.

Activities 6.4 and 6.5

What did they say? (1) and **(2)**

Activity 6.4 takes the form of a conversation between the little fox and his dad. Talk through the illustrations and establish what is happening, introducing the necessary vocabulary: the fox's *jumper* is *under* the *bed*, but he can't put it on because it's *dirty*. The children complete each sentence by choosing one of the words underneath it. In activity 6.5, the children use a similar procedure to complete each pair of sentences.

Activities 6.6 and 6.7

Make two new sentences (1) and **(2)**

There are five pairs of sentences in activity 6.6. The incomplete sentences in each pair are identical, but the children should make them different when they complete them. You may want to give an example:

This is my *old* shoe.
This is my *blue* shoe.

Explain to the children that they can choose from the bank of words at the bottom of the page or they may want to use words of their own. Help them to see that although the words are different they are the same 'sort' of word. In activity 6.7, the children are not given words to choose from and need to think of their own.

Activity 6.8

Finish the story

This activity reinforces earlier work, but involves a short continuous passage rather than isolated sentences. Talk through the text and illustrations with the children, making sure that they understand what is going on in the story and recognise any unfamiliar vocabulary. Explain that there are some words missing from the text and that they should choose from the words given to fill the gaps.

Following up

During shared writing, re-read together what you have written to make sure it makes sense. Choose a sentence and ask the children if it sounds right. Is anything missing? Deliberately leave out a word at random when reading another sentence and challenge the children to tell you what is missing.

Encourage the children to read their writing aloud to really hear if it sounds right. Suggest that they try reading out each sentence as they finish writing it. This is the first step to editing their own work.

Mind the gap

It _____ cold.

put	is	we

_____ on your hat.

Snow	Then	Put

Then _____ can go.

your	look	we

I _____ something to eat.

want	hungry	you

Do _____ want an apple?

am	eat	you

Read each sentence. Which word fits the gap? Fill in each space with the correct word.

Scholastic Literacy Skills
Grammar and punctuation

Make it fit

I _____ cold.

Look at _____ hat.

I _____ a sandwich.

Put _____ this hat.

Do _____ want an apple?

_____ you like dogs?

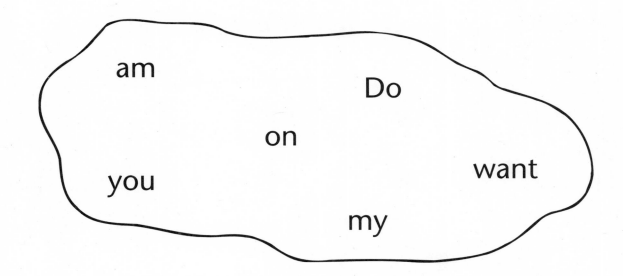

am

Do

on

you

want

my

Which of the words from the bottom of the page fits the sentence? Write it in the gap.

My brother

My _____ will be ten in _____.

Where did _____ get _____ hat?

_____ has got a _____ bike.

_____ you seen my red _____?

_____ you help _____ push this box?

We were _____ home last _____.

March	He	brother	at
night	me	book	new
Can	you	that	Have

Write the most suitable word from the bottom of the page in each gap.

Name

Unit **6** 4: What did they say? (1)

Little fox's jumper

_____ can I put on?

Bed   What   Under

Put on your _____ jumper.

red   my   not

Where _____ it?

the   for   is

It is _____ the bed.

put   your   under

Oh no! I can't _____ it on.

red   the   put

Why not?

_____ is dirty.

My   Saw   It

What are the foxes saying? Fill in each space with the correct word.

Unit **6** 5: What did they say? (2)

Name

In the box

Look _____ my cat.

It _____ in that tree.

(at   big   is   the   like)

I _____ that bike.

Is it _____ bike?

(who   like   on   your   look)

Put the toys _____.

Put the _____ in the box.

(cars   away   go   at   them)

Choose one of the words provided to finish each sentence. Write it in the gap.

Monster!

Look at the _____.

Look at the _____.

I _____ ice cream.

I _____ ice cream.

_____ saw my mum.

_____ saw my mum.

Your bag is _____ the table.

Your bag is _____ the table.

" _____ away!" shouted Matt.

" _____ away!" shouted Matt.

on   car   like   Run   under

want   Go   I   monster   Katy

Choose a word to finish each sentence. Make two different sentences in each pair.

Spiders

The flower is _____.

The flower is _____.

I _____ spiders.

I _____ spiders.

_____ went to play with Imran.

_____ went to play with Imran.

Put the _____ in the box.

Put the _____ in the box.

Think of a word to finish each sentence. Each pair should be made up of two different sentences.

Dog at school

One day, Sam went _____ school as usual.

His dog, Bingo, _____ too.

"Go home, Bingo," said _____. But Bingo

_____ not go.

"Go _____, Bingo," said Sam at lunchtime.

But _____ did not go. She was still there

_____ home time.

Then Mum came. Bingo and

Sam went home with Mum.

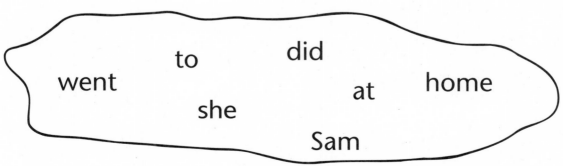

went   to   did   she   at   home   Sam

Complete the story by writing one of the words from the box in each gap.

Unit 7 Common and proper nouns

A noun is the name of a thing or a feeling. A *common noun* is the general name of something, for instance *book* or *girl.* A *proper noun* is the special name that identifies a specific thing or person, for example *Pete* or *Scotland.* This unit begins by looking at common nouns and then moves on to the names of places, people, days of the week and months of the year, all of which begin with capital letters. The use of capitalisation in book titles is also explored.

Many Year 1 classes refer to nouns as *naming words.* It is up to you to decide when it is appropriate to introduce the terms *common noun* and *proper noun.*

Contents

7.1 Things all around	**7.5** Friends
7.2 Lists	**7.6** Days of the week
7.3 Here I am	**7.7** Months of the year
7.4 Postcard	**7.8** Book titles

Objectives

- Understand the function of a 'naming word' (common noun) within a sentence.
- Recognise that common nouns can be classified into groups.
- Recognise that some words name special things and require a capital letter.
- Use a capital letter to begin names of people and places, days of the week and months of the year and main words in titles.

Ways of teaching

Explain to the children that you are going to look at words that tell us the names of things. Give them a few examples of common nouns and ask them to suggest some more. They could begin with things in the classroom, such as *book* and *table,* then go on to suggest things at home or items they eat or play with.

If children suggest *people* as one of the words, use the opportunity to introduce the idea that some naming words are special, for example the names of people or places, and that to show they are special we begin them with capital letters.

In shared reading, point out a character's name and draw attention to the capital letter. Ask the children to find this name elsewhere in the book and, on a sheet of acetate over the page, to circle the capital letter each time. Ask them to find and mark other names in the text.

Write up your own name and some of the children's names, asking them to tell you when to include capital letters. (Use a different colour for the capital letters.) Go on to demonstrate how names of places also begin with capital letters. Start with the name of your school and the town or village it is in.

About the activities

Activity 7.1 **Things all around**

Point out that many nouns can be categorised according to where we find them, for example inside or outside, at the swimming pool, in the park, at the beach and so on.

Talk briefly about the three environments on the activity sheet and ask the children what sort of things they might see there. Tell them to list as many things as they can on the sheet. Emphasise that you want them to make a list, so they should just write out the naming words and not try to put them into sentences.

Activity 7.2 **Lists**

Remind the children how to write lists and explore the idea that naming words can be collected into groups of type, for example *toys, food, things to write with* and so on. Write some of these headings on the board and ask the children to help you to list some nouns that fall into these categories.

On the activity sheet, tell the children to sort the muddled things in the star into the four lists. They may also be able to think of some extra things to add to each list. Make sure they all know the meaning of the word *furniture*.

Activity 7.3 **Here I am**

Point out that I is always a capital letter when it stands alone. The writer to whom it refers is very special. Tell the children to draw a picture of themselves and you on the sheet. They can then finish the sentences. Remind them to use capital letters to begin names and to put a full stop at the end of each sentence. Talk about who they might draw in the last box – perhaps a friend, Mum or a pet. Explain that they should choose either S*he* or H*e* to begin each of the last two sentences.

Activity 7.4 **Postcard**

Tell the children that Kim sent this postcard while on holiday in Spain, but she has left out nearly all the capital letters. Read the text through to the children, then ask them to correct it. Advise them that first they should look for the beginning of sentences and put in the capital letters there, then they should find 'special' words (proper nouns) and give them capitals. Afterwards, you could discuss how many names of people and places the children found.

To complete the second part of the activity, ask the children to imagine that Kim has sent this card to your school. Ask the children to write the school name and address on the right-hand side of the postcard, using capital letters as appropriate. If you think it would help to write the school name and address for the children to copy, ask for their help in deciding where the capital letters go.

Using a template, the children could write their own postcard, telling someone at home about what happened at school today. If they don't know their home address, you can ask them to take the postcard home and, for homework, ask someone to help them write it correctly.

Activity 7.5 **Friends**

Ask the children to think of names for the three characters in the activity. Point out that the special names of pets have capital letters like those of people.

The children should write the names again to complete the sentences below and then write two sentences of their own about the illustrations. Remind them to use full stops.

Activity 7.6 **Days of the week**
Draw the children's attention to the capital letters at the beginning of the days of the week and months of the year every time you write the day or date. Talk briefly about some of the things you do regularly on certain days of the week and then ask the children to complete the sentences in the activity, listing one or two things that they do each day. You may want to develop this into a simple class timetable. Finally, encourage the children to write about their favourite day of the week, explaining why it is their favourite.

Activity 7.7 **Months of the year**
Introduce the months of the year and the seasons. Talk about which months fall into which season. Write the months on the board in seasonal groups, emphasising the capital letter at the beginning of each month. Discuss which months are special for the children – because of festivals, holidays, birthdays or other special events.

Ask a child in which month his or her birthday falls. Is anyone else born in the same month? Ask everyone to complete the sentences in the activity, adding full stops. Let them know that there is more than one correct answer for the hot or cold months.

With your help, the children could develop work on the months of the year by conducting a survey of which months everyone was born in and make a bar chart to record the information.

Activity 7.8 **Book titles**
During shared reading, point out the capital letters in book titles. By looking at several book titles, help the children to see that the first word always has a capital letter and so do the other main words. Point out that the 'small' words, such as *the*, *and*, *on* and *in*, often do not have capital letters as they are less important.

Write, in all lower-case letters, the titles of some books you have in the classroom and invite children to come out and put the capitals where they think they should be. Ask the other children to help and comment. Then compare the children's versions with copies of the books.

Ask the children to write the titles on the book covers in the activity, using capital letters appropriately. Encourage them to use the information in the picture to come up with their own title for the last book.

Invite the children to look back at the last story they wrote and see if they used capital letters properly in the title.

Following up Invite the children to go on a hunt for proper nouns in the classroom or around the school. They could write them down and then feed back to a plenary session in which you can talk about where and why the proper nouns have been used.

Give each group a book to look through for capital letters. Ask them to pick out all the different reasons capital letters are used, then feed back to the class with examples.

Out and about

What things would you see in these places? Write their names in lists.

at home	in the street	in the park

What is it?

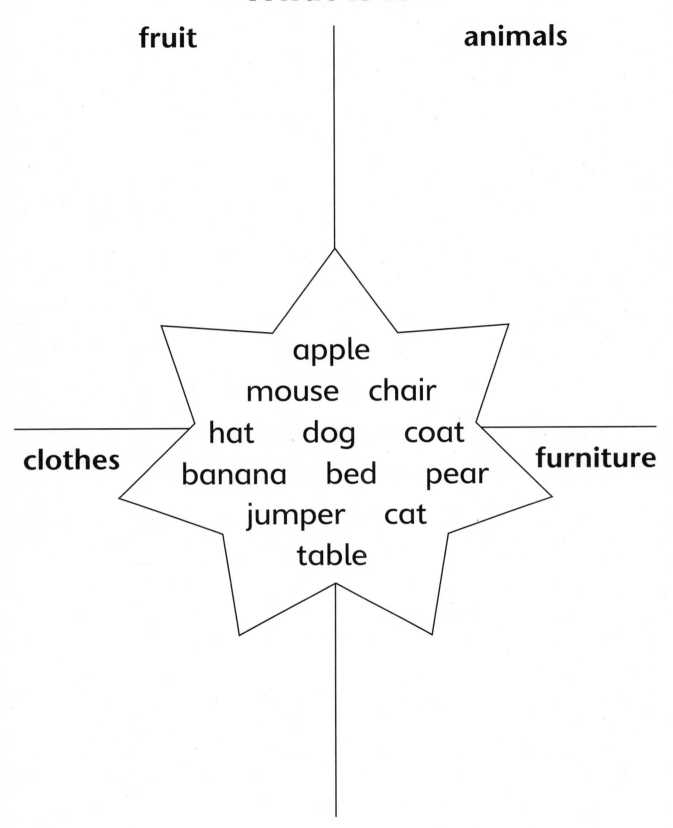

fruit   **animals**

clothes

apple

mouse   chair

hat   dog   coat

banana   bed   pear

jumper   cat

table

furniture

Sort these naming words into groups. If you can think of more things that fit into any of the groups, add their names.

Here I am

Here I am.

My name is _____

This is my teacher.

_____ is called _____

| He | She |

This is my _____

_____ is called _____

| He | She |

Draw yourself in the top box. Draw your teacher in the second box. Finish the sentences. Remember to use capital letters and full stops in the right places. Draw something or someone else in the last box and finish that sentence.

On holiday

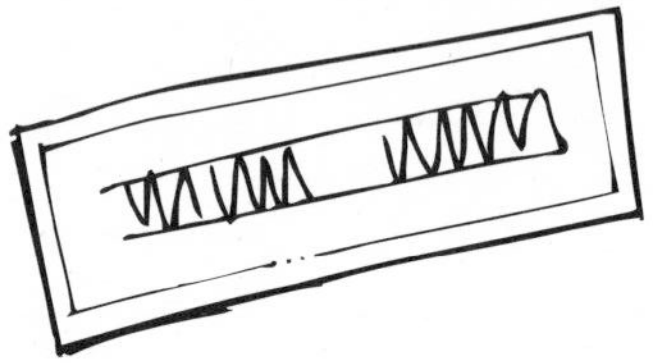

Hello everyone

we are on holiday in spain.

dan and i are having a great

time. we will see you soon.

Love from

kim

Put in six capital letters. Write your school address on the right.

In the park with...

_____   _____   _____

Here is _____

Look at _____ and

_____

_____

_____

_____

Make up names for these characters and write the names under the pictures. Complete the sentences by adding the names. Then finish the story.

My favourite day

Monday   Tuesday   Wednesday

Thursday   Friday   Saturday   Sunday

At school...

On _____ we _____

On _____ we _____

On _____ we _____

On _____ we _____

On _____ we _____

On _____ and _____ we don't

go to school.

My favourite day of the week is _____ because

_____

_____

_____

Complete the sentences. Remember that days of the week always start with a capital letter.

My best month

January   February   March   April   May
June   July   August   September
October   November   December

Today's date is _____

My birthday is in _____

It is cold in _____

Sometimes it is hot in _____

The month I like best is _____ because

_____

_____

_____

Complete the sentences, adding full stops at the end. Remember that months of the year always start with a capital letter.

Story book covers

the little red hen

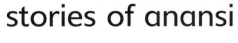

stories of anansi

goldilocks and the
three bears

Write the titles on the book covers, putting capital letters in the right places. Then make up a title for the last book.

Capitalisation

Use capital letters to begin:

special names...

...of people	My name is **A**nna.
	My teacher is **M**r **B**enn.
...pets	The dog is called **B**ingo.
...places	I live in **H**ull.
	Gran's house is in **L**ong **R**oad.
...days	We go swimming on **M**onday.
...months	My birthday is in **A**pril.

the first word and the main words in titles...

...of books	**G**oldilocks and the **T**hree **B**ears
...stories	**T**he **S**tory of the **L**ady **P**irate
...TV programmes	**B**lue **P**eter

Verb tenses

Today	Yesterday
We **walk** up the hill.	We **walked** up the hill.
I **look** at the hats.	We **looked** at the hats.
I **see** a cat.	I **saw** a cat.
I **go** to school.	I **went** to school.
We **say,** "Hello."	We **said,** "Hello."
We **make** a mess.	We **made** a mess.
I **buy** a new book.	I **bought** a new book.

What are they saying?

Dad said, "I'm going out."

"I like swimming," said Kay.

I shouted, "Look out!"

"How old are you?" asked Tim.

"I'm hiding," whispered Allan.

"Stop!" yelled the policeman.

I'm going out.

I like swimming.

Look out!

How old are you?

I'm hiding.

Stop!

Unit ① Sentences

A sentence is a unit of language that makes sense on its own. It can be a statement or a question. In writing, a sentence begins with a capital letter and ends with a full stop, question mark or exclamation mark.

It can take a long time for some children to feel secure with what differentiates a group of words or a line of writing from a sentence. Continue to draw attention to sentences during shared reading and writing and focus regularly on the children's written work as a source of sentences.

Contents

1.1 Find the sentences
1.2 Make sentences (1)
1.3 Make sentences (2)
1.4 Find sentences in instructions
1.5 Find sentences in a poem (1)
1.6 Find sentences in a poem (2)
1.7 Use words to make a sentence

1.8 Tell a story
1.9 Sort out questions and answers
1.10 Exclamation mark or question mark?
1.11 Full stop or question mark?
1.12 Put in the punctuation

Objectives
- Recognise the difference between a phrase and a sentence.
- Understand that a sentence must make sense.
- Recognise when a sentence should end with a full stop, an exclamation mark or a question mark.
- Use sentences in their own writing.

Ways of teaching

Recap what the children know about sentences – they
- begin with a capital letter
- end with a full stop, an exclamation mark or a question mark
- make sense on their own
- are not the same as a line of text.

Reiterate to the children that a sentence is not necessarily the same as a printed line of text. On a page of a Big Book, find a line of text that comprises one complete sentence plus the beginning of another. Cover up the rest of the text, then read the line. Ask the children if it is a sentence. Ask them where the sentence is. Where does it end? Someone could show you by using Blu-Tack to indicate the capital letter that begins the sentence and the full stop that ends it. Now focus on the second, unfinished sentence. Does it make sense? Is it finished? Ask the children to suggest ways of completing it. See if they can prompt you to add the appropriate punctuation mark at the end.

Cover up all of the text on another Big Book page. Ask several children to say one sentence each about the illustration. Write their sentences on the board, asking all the children to tell you how to begin it (with a capital letter) and what punctuation to put at the end. Do the same with several consecutive pages of the book.

About the activities

Activity 1.1

Find the sentences

Read the story to the children, then explain that the writer has forgotten to put the capital letter at the beginning of each sentence and the full stop at the end. When the children have put in the capital letters and full stops, ask them to write two sentences of their own about something they have made.

Encourage them to check some of their other writing for sentences – paying attention to sense and punctuation.

Activities 1.2 and 1.3

Make sentences (1) and **(2)**

Children can work individually or in pairs to make as many complete sentences as they can, using the words on the sheets. It will be easier if they can cut out the words and move them around to make sentences. Advise the children that each time they make a sentence, they should write it down, remembering to use a capital letter and a full stop, and that they can use the words as often as they like. Draw their attention to the blank box in activity 1.2 for them to add a word of their own.

This exercise can be turned into a game by giving several mixed-ability pairs a time limit. For example, see which pair can come up with the most sentences in five minutes.

Activity 1.4

Find sentences in instructions

Explain to the children that a girl wrote these instructions to tell someone how to get from her school to Long Meadow, but she didn't show any sentences. Read through the text with the children, then ask them to work on it in pairs. They should read it aloud, paying attention to where they naturally pause, then add the capital letters and full stops as appropriate. Let them know that there are seven sentences. Explain that marking out the sentences in this way will help to make the meaning clear and they can then follow the instructions to draw the route on the map.

Pairs or groups of children could then talk about how to get from the classroom to another place in the school, such as the playground or the secretary's office. (You may want to suggest an appropriate place.) The children may need to walk the route and talk through the instructions with an adult. Working together, the children should write down their instructions in sentences. Encourage them to re-read their writing for sense and punctuation.

Activities 1.5 and 1.6

Find sentences in a poem (1) and **(2)**

Explain to the children that, in this special instance, each line of writing *should* be a sentence, as that is the way these poems are arranged. Both of these activities are worked on in the same way, but 1.6 will suit more able children. Other children may work in mixed-ability pairs or groups.

In each case, read through the poem. Tell the children that 'Snow' has four sentences and 'Moods' has three. Ask the children to read the poem again themselves and mark where the sentences begin and end. Then they should write out the poem, starting each sentence on a new line.

Alternatively, the children could shade each sentence in a different colour and then cut them out, sticking them down in the form of poems, with each sentence starting on a new line. Advise them that the last sentence in each poem is quite long and may run over onto two lines.

See 'Following up' for ways of using 'Moods' as a model for the children to write their own poems in sentences.

Activity 1.7

Use words to make a sentence

The children should make up sentences that use the words given on the activity sheet, but let them know that they will need to add extra words of their own to make the sentences complete and funny. They can also use the words in any order. Remind them to use capital letters and full stops and then ask them to illustrate one of their sentences in the box.

Activity 1.8

Tell a story

Talk through the pictures to tell the story of the Gingerbread Man. You may like to write some useful vocabulary on the board.

Ask the children to write a sentence next to each picture on the sheet, to describe what is happening. Explain that the aim is to tell the story in four sentences. Encourage higher-ability children to go back and write a second sentence about each picture.

Activity 1.9

Sort out questions and answers

Ask the children if the sets of words on the sheet are sentences. Can they tell you why not? At the moment, they don't make sense and the children's task is to sort them out so that they do. Each pair consists of a question and an answer. The capital letters and question marks have been included to show where the sentences begin and where the questions end, but the children will have to make up their own minds about where to put the full stops in the answer sentences.

Activity 1.10

Exclamation mark or question mark?

Introduce exclamation marks to the children and explain that they are used at the end of sentences where somebody shouts, or is surprised, cross or excited. Write a couple of examples on the board, such as *Help*! *Oh no*! *Stop that*! Ask the children how to read these sentences aloud with the right intonation. Write a few questions, for example *Where are you going*? *Are you cold*? and together compare the way these would be read aloud, emphasising intonation and tone of voice.

Read through the questions and exclamations in the activity and ask the children to put in the appropriate punctuation marks. Ask them to practise saying the sentences out loud to a partner (without shouting!). They should then think of one question to ask their partner and one surprised or angry sentence to 'shout' at them. (Make sure everyone knows that they must not write anything hurtful.)

Activity 1.11

Full stop or exclamation mark?

Ask the children to practise reading these sentences aloud in different ways. Which ones would they normally say in a loud voice? Tell them to choose whether to put a full stop or an exclamation mark at the end of every sentence, using three of each altogether.

What do the children think the characters in the pictures are saying? Are any of them shouting? Ask the children to write a sentence of speech for each character, reminding them to use exclamation marks only if the person is shouting, cross or surprised. The children can decide if the man or the child is speaking in the last picture, or even write speech for both characters if they feel confident.

Activity 1.12   **Put in the punctuation**

Explain that the activity shows a dialogue between two children. Talk through the lines of speech and the pictures with the children. Ask them to work in pairs, each taking a role, and to read the words aloud. Advise the children to think how the characters would say the words and what tells them about the punctuation needed. Is it a question, a statement or an exclamation?

When the children have added the punctuation, they should read the dialogue aloud again and ask themselves if it sounds right. Advise them that they might find it helpful to cross out the punctuation marks at the top of the sheet as they are used.

Finally, ask the children to think what the characters might say next and write some words of their own in the speech bubbles. Remind them to consider the punctuation.

Following up   Use 'Moods' (in activity 1.5) as a model for the children to write their own poems, using three sentences, each of which starts on a new line. For example:

> I have lots of moods.
> When I am in a bad mood I _____.
> When I am in a good mood I _____.

The children could extend their poems by writing a few more sentences about being in a funny or cross mood. Alternatively, they could leave out the word *mood* and include other feelings, for example When I *am unhappy/happy/jealous/ excited/scared* I _____.

Point out to the children that usually somebody *does* something in a sentence, and ask them to identify who does what in a variety of sentences, both that they have heard or read before and that are new to them.

Working in pairs, the children could write down three words each and swap them with their partners. Each child then has to make up a sentence using the words they have been given. This could be an oral or written activity, and the same exercise could be used to make a question.

Peter's monster

Find seven sentences in this story. Change any letters that should be capitals and add the full stops.

Peter made a monster it was bigger than he was Peter gave his monster a hat he gave it a coat he gave it glasses he put the monster in a chair it gave the teacher a fright

Write two sentences about something **you** have made.

_____

_____

_____

_____

Word jumble (1)

How many sentences can you make from the words at the bottom of the page? Add your own word in the blank box and use that too. Write down each sentence as you make it.

_____

_____

_____

_____

_____

_____

_____

_____

school	I	went	
like	swimming	to	
chocolate	park	don't	.
dogs	the		we

Word jumble (2)

How many sentences can you make from the words
at the bottom of the page? Write your sentences here:

_____

_____

_____

_____

_____

_____

_____

_____

they	ball	played	car
wanted	old	took	.
with	new	I	my
a	you	had	

How to get to Long Meadow

Add the missing full stops and capital letters
to these sentences.

first you go out of the school gate turn left and go along Kingston Road next you turn right down Long Road and go past the shop go over the bridge walk down past the car park soon you will be in Long Meadow

Which way did the writer go? Draw her route on the map.

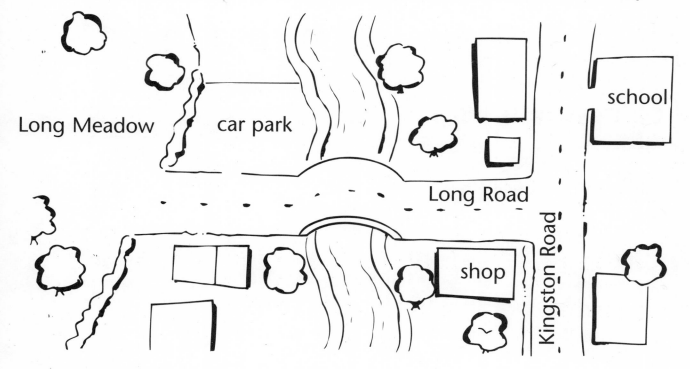

Explain how to get from your classroom to another place in the school. Write your instructions in sentences.

Moods

Find the sentences in this poem.
Write out the poem in sentences. Start each sentence on a
new line and remember to add capital letters and full stops.

i have lots of moods when I

am in a bad mood I unroll

the toilet roll when I am in a good mood I

roll up the toilet roll

Robert Whitson (age 6)

_____

_____

_____

_____

_____

Scholastic Literacy Skills
Grammar and punctuation

📖 S C H O L A S T I C   photocopiable

Snow

Find the sentences and write out the poem. Start each
sentence on a new line, adding capital letters and full stops.

it is winter time the snow is

falling the grass looks like sticks of glass the

road is covered with a white sheet

for cars to draw on

Peter Bradley (age 7)

_____

_____

_____

_____

Silly sentences

Make a sentence from each of these sets of words.
Add some of your own words and try to make the
sentences as funny as you can.

(pizza jam put) _____

_____

(ran magic shoes) _____

_____

(teacher funny hat) _____

_____

(jumped ghost window) _____

_____

Illustrate one of
your sentences.

The Gingerbread Man

Tell the story by writing a sentence for each picture.
Use the words from the bottom of the page.

_____

_____

_____

_____

_____

_____

_____

_____

_____

Gingerbread Man   oven   ran away

Questions and answers

Rewrite these questions and answers so that they make sense. Add the full stops.

you   my   Have   seen   book?
is   on   table   It   the

_____

_____

bike?   do   your   ride   you   Where
park   the   ride   bike   I   in   my

_____

_____

When   we   playground?   to   go   can   the
tea   can   after   We   go

_____

_____

your   Is   at   sister   home?
shops   at   is   She   the   Dad   with

_____

_____

Scholastic Literacy Skills
Grammar and punctuation
■ S C H O L A S T I C   photocopiable

! or ?

Put a question mark or an exclamation mark at the end of each sentence. Try saying the sentences aloud to help you to decide which to use.

Look at that

It's enormous

Do you want a sweet

Can we go out now

Is that your cat

I won't go to bed

That's great

I love chocolate

Where are my shoes

Who is that boy

Write a question to ask your partner.

_____

_____

Write a sentence you would shout.

_____

_____

. or !

Put in the full stops and exclamation marks.

Look out

I am looking for my gloves

Go away

I hate spiders

He is watching TV

We came on the bus

What are these people saying? Write a sentence of speech for each person, including a full stop or exclamation mark.

_____

_____

_____

_____

_____

_____

Catch!

Put these punctuation marks in the right places: **! ! ? ? ? . .**

Come and play

What do you want to play

Can we play catch

Yes. Here's a ball

Can you catch this

Watch out

Help

What did they say next?

Unit 2 Proper nouns

There are four types of noun:
- *Common nouns* are names of things and refer to any example of the type, for example *cat*.
- *Proper nouns* always begin with a capital letter. They are special names that identify a specific place or person, such as *Sanjay* or *Glasgow*, the day of the week or the month of the year.
- *Collective nouns* refer to a group of things, such as a *crowd* of people.
- *Abstract nouns* refer to non-concrete things like *misery* or *idea*.
This unit focuses on proper nouns and helps children to see when they should use capital letters to start words other than at the beginning of a sentence.

Contents
2.1 Yourself and other animals
2.2 Capital letters for people and places
2.3 Capital letters in a story
2.4 Make up people and places for a story
2.5 Days of the week
2.6 Story titles

Objectives
- Recognise proper nouns.
- Know when to use capitalisation, for example for names and titles.

Ways of teaching
Display Poster 1 in the classroom. It supports the work in this unit by giving examples, in context, of the 'special' words that must begin with a capital letter. Remind the children that names of people, places and animals are special words and always begin with a capital letter. Encourage the children to spot proper nouns in the books they are reading and on signs around the school.

Recap on when to use capital letters in titles (on the first word and other main words). Hide the title of a Big Book you have recently read together, then write the title, all in lower case, on the board. Ask which words should have capital letters. Display the book title. Were the children right? Repeat this exercise with several other books.

About the activities

Activity 2.1 **Yourself and other animals**
Tell the children that they are going to write about themselves and make up names for some animals. They should then write about two of the animals they have named. The names and sentences should reflect the animal characteristics that the children are thinking about.

Activities 2.2 and 2.3 **Capital letters for people and places** and **Capital letters in a story**
Write your own name on the board, pointing out that a capital letter is used for your title. Ask the children for the names of some other adults they know, for example the headteacher, the caretaker, Aunty _____, Doctor _____, and ask the children to tell you when to use capitals as you write these names on the board. Now ask them to name some of the places they have been to or would like to go to, and write these up, emphasising the capital letters.

Read through the sentences in activity 2.2 and ask the children to look for the special words that need capitals. Remind them that a word like *cats*, for example, doesn't require a capital because it is not the special name of a particular cat. When they have completed the activity, the children could go on to make two lists on another sheet of paper – one of people and the other of places – starting with those on the activity sheet, then adding their own.

Read through activity 2.3 together and tell the children to look out for the names of people and places. Explain that they should cross out the initial letter and write a capital above it. They should also put capitals at the beginning of sentences. Point out that the title needs correcting too. Ask the children to make a list the people and places mentioned. The children can then continue the story, going onto the back of the sheet.

Activity 2.4

Make up people and places for a story

Tell the children that they are going to write a story about a journey on a magic bus. Ask them where they would like to go if a magic bus picked them up. Write up some of the place names they suggest, asking what you should put at the beginning of the words (capital letters).

Read through the activity together, pointing out the commas that will separate their lists of people and place names. When they have completed the sentences, see if they can continue the story.

Activity 2.5

Days of the week

Remind the children that days of the week and months of the year always begin with a capital letter. Explain that this timetable shows what Tom does on each school day and they should use the information to complete the sentences. Then ask the children to write a sentence or two about what they get up to at weekends.

Activity 2.6

Story titles

Show the children some magazine photographs of people doing things. Ask the children to think of names for the people and a title for each picture. Write these on the board, asking the children to tell you where to use capital letters.

Without using capital letters, write the titles of some familiar stories on the board. Ask the children to decide which words should be capitalised.

Go on to tell the children that each of the pictures in activity 2.6 is from a story. They should try to imagine what each story is about and invent a title for it, taking care to use capital letters correctly.

Following up

Find examples of capital letters used for emphasis in a Big Book and establish with the children how they should be read aloud. Write some sentences (such as *What is that mess?* or *That's mine!*) and ask the children to select one word in each to say loudly (stress). Rewrite the sentence with the chosen word in capitals and ask the children to say it aloud. Experiment with a variety of sentences, putting different words in capitals and saying them together.

Me and my animals

Write about yourself. Remember to use capitals to begin names and places.

My name is_____

I live in a place called_____

Two people in my family are_____

and_____

If I had a dog I would call it_____

If I had a fish I would call it_____

Think of names for these animals:

_____ _____ _____

Choose two of them and write one sentence about each.

_____

_____

■SCHOLASTIC   photocopiable

People and places

These sentences all begin with capital letters, but there are other capital letters missing. Rewrite the sentences, putting all the capital letters in the right places.

I went to see aunty suzie.

_____

I got a card from america.

_____

Did you see joe?

_____

They are going to london.

_____

I went to southport last week.

_____

My teacher is miss dean.

_____

My uncle tim lives in blackpool.

_____

His cats are called patch and poppy.

_____

Name

the giant of biggin hill

Put capital letters in the right places and continue the story.

once there was a giant called max. he lived on biggin hill in upland. max had a dog called kelly, but he had no friends.

in the nearby village of snooze lived a young girl called eliza. eliza lived with her brother, jim and her sisters, lucy and anna.

every day, max watched eliza take jim, lucy and anna to school. he saw her clean the house and feed the animals. eliza worked hard and max felt sorry for her.

one day, _____

_____

Make lists of...

...characters in the story   ...places in the story

_____   _____

_____   _____

_____   _____

_____

◣ SCHOLASTIC photocopiable

The magic bus

Write the names of the people who went on the bus and the places it went to. Remember to include capital letters.

I went on a magic bus.

I took four people with me.

They were _____, _____,

_____ and _____.

The bus set off.

We went to four places.

We went to _____,

_____,

_____ and _____.

We stopped at _____

and we all got out. Then we had a big

surprise.

What happened?

_____

_____

_____

_____

Tom's timetable

Finish the sentences and answer the questions to describe Tom's week.

Monday	Tuesday	Wednesday	Thursday	Friday
PE	cooking	assembly	library	swimming

Saturday	Sunday

Tom does cooking on _____

Tom does PE on _____

He has assembly on _____

What day does he go swimming?
_____

What day does he go to the library?
_____

What do you do on Saturday and Sunday? Fill in your timetable, then use the back of the sheet to write sentences about what you do.

What's the story?

Each of these pictures is from a story. Give each story a title.

_____

_____

_____

_____

_____

_____

Write the title of the last story you wrote.

_____

Write the title of a book you like.

_____

Unit 3 Questions

Children will gradually learn that some sentences *give* information and others *ask* for information. Having explored statements in the previous two units, the children now move on to questions.

First, the unit looks at question words and sorting groups of words from complete questions, then it moves on to changing sentences into questions and encouraging children to think of their own questions.

Contents

3.1 Question words
3.2 Compile a questionnaire
3.3 Ask questions (imaginative context)
3.4 Ask questions (non-fiction)
3.5 Ask questions (fictional character)

3.6 Turn statements into questions (1)
3.7 Turn statements into questions (2)
3.8 Turn statements into questions (3)
3.9 Colour questions
3.10 What did they ask?

Objectives

- Use *wh* words to open questions.
- Turn statements into questions.
- Pose questions of their own.

Ways of teaching

Tell the children that there is a group of words that are often used to begin questions. They begin with W*h*. Can the children tell you what they are? (W*hat, where, who, why, when*.) As each one is introduced, ask the children to give examples of questions that begin with that word.

Advise the children that we can also make questions *without* these words. Ask them to suggest a few examples of this sort of question. If this is difficult, offer a few words that might begin such questions (usually verbs), for example *Can I… Is it… Are you…*

Look through a Big Book together and identify questions in the text. Do they all begin with *wh* question words? How can we tell they are sentences? How would the children say them aloud?

Ask the children to point out questions in their reading books and in their own writing.

Make a simple sentence using high-frequency words, such as I*t is a car*. Show the children how you can make this into a question by rearranging the words and adding a question mark instead of the full stop – I*s it a car*? Work through some more examples together.

About the activities

Activity 3.1

Question words

Ask the children what are the *wh* words that so often start questions and invite them to ask questions, using each one. Tell them that all the questions in the activity are missing their question word. Advise them to read each question first and put in the *wh* word that makes sense.

Activity 3.2

Compile a questionnaire

The children should work in pairs to complete this activity. Introduce questionnaires by writing *When, Where, Why, What* and *Who* underneath each other on the board and asking several children a simple question to go with each, for example *Where is your bag? When do you have lunch? What colour is your jumper?* Then invite the children to think of their own questions to ask someone else.

Activity 3.3

Ask questions (imaginative context)

Talk briefly about the picture on the sheet. What do the children think is happening? Does it remind anyone of a story they know? (Maybe 'Jack and the Beanstalk'.) What questions does the picture make the children want to ask? (*Where does the ladder go to? Who put it there? Why doesn't it fall down? What might happen?*) Ask the children to write four questions about the picture and then a sentence or two to say what might have happened next.

This work can be used as the starting point for a story, with the children using their questions to plan what problem the two children encounter and how it is all sorted out in the end.

Activity 3.4

Ask questions (non-fiction)

When the children are going to research and write about something, it will help if they can think of questions to which they would like answers.

The children can work on this activity in pairs or groups, thinking of questions they would like to ask about this dinosaur. For example, *What type of dinosaur is it? What did they eat?* and so on. Emphasise that they should be asking questions *about* dinosaurs and not direct questions *to* this one (*Where did they live?* not *Where did you live?*).

Share some of the questions at the end of the session and see if anyone can provide answers. To demonstrate how to look for answers, choose two or three questions that can be answered by books you have available.

If you have a computer program or access to online information about dinosaurs, this activity can be used to lead in to an ICT session. Tell the children that you are going to look at some information about dinosaurs on the computer, but first you want them to think about what they would like to find out.

Activity 3.5

Ask questions (fictional character)

Tell the children to imagine they have met this giant. What three questions would they like to ask him? They may use the words in the box to help them to think of ideas. Advise them that they can use the *wh* question words if they wish. Then ask them to write a sentence giving the giant's answer to one of their questions. They could then go on to answer their other questions, using the back of the sheet.

This work can be the basis of a character portrait that the children can use to write a story about their giant.

| Activities 3.6 to 3.8 | **Turn statements into questions (1) to (3)** |

Turn statements into questions (1) to **(3)**

Draw a simple sketch of a person on the board and make a statement about the figure, for example *This is Jake*. Explain to the children that if you weren't sure who the boy was you might ask a question about him, such as *Is this Jake*? Show the children how to rearrange the words to form a question and ask them what you must put at the end (a question mark). Write out a few more simple sentences like this and ask the children to rearrange them into questions.

The task in each of these activities is to rearrange the statements into questions, without using additional words. In activity 3.6, the first word of each question has been provided. Remind the children to end every question with a question mark. When they have written their questions, ask the children to read aloud each statement and corresponding question. Encourage them to vary the intonation in their voices according to the punctuation.

Activity 3.9

Colour questions

Read the poem aloud, then read the five answer sentences given beneath it. Explain to the children that you would like them to write the questions that must have been asked to get these answers. You may like to ask them to help you with an example, such as *A cow is brown*. Question: *What is brown*? Then, ask the children to make up their own answer to the question *What is red*? Stress that their answers should be different from the poet's *poppy*.

Do the children know any more rhymes with questions in them? For example:

How many miles to Babylon?
Three score miles and ten.
Will I get there by candle light?
Yes, and back again.

Mary, Mary quite contrary,
How does your garden grow?
With cockle shells and silver bells
And pretty maids all in a row.

Ask the children to look in a variety of texts (fiction and non-fiction) to find questions, and share them in a plenary session. Talk about the different types of questions that have been found – those using *wh* words and those constructed from rearranged statements.

Activity 3.10

What did they ask?

Two puppets or soft toys might be useful in helping the children to think of questions to match the answers given in the activity. Have Puppet 1 say, for example, *My name is* _____, and tell the children that this is the answer to Puppet 2's question. What do they think Puppet 2 might have asked? Act out the children's suggestions and see if the question fits the answer each time. When the children have given a suitable question, repeat the game with another sample answer, such as *My shoes are black* or *I'm in the classroom*. Remind the children of the different types of questions they found in various texts (see Activity 3.9, above).

Explain to the children that five children each asked Amit a question, the answers to which are on the sheet. Ask the children to read each answer and think about what question Amit might have been asked. The likely questions include *How old are you?* so write up the question word *how* if it is unfamiliar. The children should then reverse the process to think of another question to ask Amit, and also invent his answer.

Following up   Invent a person (you could use an illustration or a large collage portrait) and, in shared writing, think of a series of questions about him or her. For example, *Where does he live? Has he got any brothers or sisters? What does he like to do/eat/wear? What is special about him?* Encourage the children to think of the answers and write them out to make a full character portrait. The character could also be used in a collaborative wall story.

Talk about what questions the children might want to ask their grandparents about life when their grandparents were little. For example, *Did you have a computer? What did you do at weekends? Where did you live? What was school like?* Ask the children to write down some of the questions and take them home to ask their grandparents, either on the phone or when they visit. Get together later to compare the replies.

Ask the children to choose a simple non-fiction book to look through. They should write down a question, the answer to which they know can be found in the book, and then give the book and question to a partner. (Explain that, if it is a long book, they should tell their partner on which page or in which section they will find the answer.)

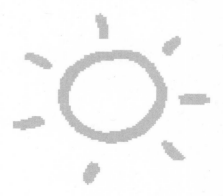

Which question word?

Put in the question word.

_____ are you going?

_____ is that boy?

_____ are you going to do?

_____ is Ben coming back?

_____ is for tea?

_____ are you crying?

_____ can we go home?

_____ are my shoes?

Why   Who

Where   When

What

Questionnaire

Make a questionnaire. Think of five questions to ask a partner. Swap papers and answer each other's questions.

1. What _____

1. _____

2. When _____

2. _____

3. Where _____

3. _____

4. Who _____

4. _____

5. Why _____

5. _____

The ladder

What questions would you ask about this picture?

Why _____

_____

_____

What _____

_____

_____

Where _____

_____

Who _____

_____

What do you think happened next?

_____

_____

_____

All about dinosaurs

What would you like to know about dinosaurs?
Ask four questions.

When _____

_____

Where _____

_____

Why _____

_____

What _____

_____

The giant

Ask the giant three questions.
The words below may give you some ideas.

1. _____

_____

2. _____

_____

3. _____

_____

eat   happy
live   sleep   friends
play   pets

Now imagine you are the giant, and answer
one of the questions.

_____

_____

Turn it around (1)

Turn these sentences into questions. Think about what you
need to add at the end of each one.

It is hot.

Is _____

I can put this hat on.

Can _____

That dog is old.

Is _____

We are going out.

Are _____

We can play football.

Can _____

They are going to school.

Are _____

Turn it around (2)

Turn these sentences into questions.

This is my book.

_____

You are my friend.

_____

He is six.

_____

You can skip.

_____

That cat is old.

_____

Your shoes are black.

_____

Turn it around (3)

Turn these sentences into questions.

That is my ball.

_____

My dog is in the house.

_____

That is Lou's mum.

_____

We can go swimming.

_____

Your hands are dirty.

_____

Grandpa is very old.

_____

The little boy was playing.

_____

We can go shopping now.

_____

What is red?

What is pink? A rose is pink
  By the fountain's brink.
What is red? A poppy's red
  In its barley bed.

Christina Rossetti

Look at the poem. Then write questions for these answers.

_____ A leaf is green.

_____ The sun is yellow.

_____ The sky is blue.

_____ A cloud is white.

_____ The night is black.

Write your own answer to this question.

What is red? _____

Ask Amit

What did the children ask? Write the questions.

_____
_____

My name
is Amit.

_____
_____

I am six
years old.

_____
_____

I like
computer
games.

_____
_____

I live in Wales.

_____
_____

Mum is
at work.

Think of another question to ask Amit.

_____

Write his answer.

_____

Unit 4 Grammatical awareness

We demonstrate grammatical awareness every time we speak. We don't need to be able to name 'nouns' and 'verbs' in order to use them. Children understand quite quickly how to put together different parts of speech in order to make meaning, and they use this understanding to check whether or not what they are reading or writing 'sounds right'.

The activities in this unit build on the corresponding ones from the first part of this book and invite children to choose the correct words to complete sentences, stories and verses of a poem. The important thing is for the children to offer the right part of speech each time.

Contents

4.1 Find two different words to fit
4.2 Cloze – finish the story

4.3 Cloze – write more verses
4.4 Cloze – tell the story

Objectives

● Recognise when a sentence makes sense.
● Use grammar to decipher new and unfamiliar text.

Ways of teaching

Understanding that only a certain kind of word will 'fit' a given space in a sentence is an important decoding skill to have. It's a skill that can be practised regularly in shared and guided reading by covering up a word in a text and asking the children to suggest a variety of possibilities for what it might be.

Write a sentence with a word missing on the board, for example I *ate a _____ for lunch*. Then write up a selection of words, from various parts of speech, such as *running, banana, big, sandwich, loudly*. Invite the children to try out the words one by one and discuss the effect. Which ones make sense? See if the children can suggest more possible words, including some funny or unlikely ones, such as *house* and *kangaroo*. Help the children to see that all the possible ones are the same sort of word; in this case, nouns or naming words. Repeat the process, omitting a different part of speech from a sentence, for example *The girl _____ the cat*.

When the children have completed any of the following activities you may want to draw their attention to the *type* of word that is appropriate in each exercise – naming words, doing words and describing words. Begin a list of all the words the children used to fill a single gap and ask them to suggest more words of the same type to add to the list.

About the activities

Activity 4.1 **Find two different words to fit**

This activity follows on naturally from the introductory exercise in 'Ways of teaching'. The words that fit in sentences 1 and 2 will be verbs, 3 is an adjective, 4 a noun and 5 another adjective. 6 could be the definite article (*the*) or a possessive pronoun (*his*, *my* and so on) or even a name with an apostrophe (*Pete's*). Tell the children to say their two sentences quietly to themselves to make sure that they 'sound' right.

Activity 4.2 **Cloze – finish the story**

In the first part of the activity, the children are given a choice of words to use to complete the sentences. In the second part, they need to think of their own words. Invite them to make their sentences as funny or preposterous as they want. They will enjoy illustrating their 'stories' afterwards. When writing their own cloze sentences, see if the children's partners come up with different words to those the writers were thinking of.

Activity 4.3 **Cloze – write more verses**

Read through the poem a couple of times together, then make sure the children can read the words from the wordbank. Explain to them that they are going to write more verses of the poem by changing some of the words, choosing a word from the bank to fill each gap. Remind the children that they will have to use the same type of word as has been taken out, otherwise the poem won't make sense.

Activity 4.4 **Cloze – tell the story**

Explain to the children that you want them to fill in the gaps to complete the sentences and tell a story. Let them know that it doesn't really matter what words they use as long as they are the right *type* of word. Tell the children that when they have filled the gaps, you want them to decide what happens next and carry on with the story.

Following up

After shared reading of a Big Book text, use Post-it Notes to cover a number of words at random. Offer the children a list of possible replacement words to fill the gaps. Talk together about which of the words 'work' and which ones don't.

Tell the children that, together, you are going to write your own version of a familiar story from a Big Book. Share the text and, with the children's contributions, change the name of the characters, where they went, what they said, whether they sat on, under or behind the bed, and so on. Try to change a variety of different parts of speech and point out to the children that, in each case, you can only substitute the same sort of word as that you have deleted.

Fill the gap

Think of two words to fill each gap to make
two different sentences each time.

1 Katy _____ to school.

_____

2 Can you _____ the ball?

_____

3 Put on your _____ hat.

_____

4 The _____ is in the car.

_____

5 I like the _____ flowers best.

_____

6 Where are _____ shoes?

_____

Scholastic Literacy Skills
Grammar and punctuation

A monster and a puppy

Fill the gaps to tell the story.
Use some of the words from the box below.

The monster picked the flowers.

The monster _____ the flowers.

The monster ate the _____.

The teacher shouted _____ the

monster.

> broke   children   licked   at   chairs
> ate   on   flowers

_____

Think of your own words to fill these gaps.

My puppy _____ under the bed.

My puppy jumped on the _____.

I took my _____ puppy for a walk.

Now write your own sentence
with a gap and ask a friend to fill it in.

Open the door

Read the first verse of this poem, then fill in the gaps
to write three more verses.

Open the door.
What do I see?
A little black dog
Looking at me.

Open the _____.
What do I see?
A little _____ dog
Looking at me.

Open the door.
What do I see?
A little black _____
_____ at me.

Open the _____.
What do I see?
A little _____ _____
_____ at me.

brown

staring

mouse

cupboard

pointing

door

rabbit

laughing

grinning

cat

shouting

fat

box

old

Scholastic Literacy Skills
Grammar and punctuation

■ S C H O L A S T I C   photocopiable

Once there was...

Add words to tell this story. Then write what happens next.
Illustrate your story.

Once there was a little _____.

He _____ in a forest. He had

_____ friends.

   One day, _____ went

_____ a walk. It was very cold

and very _____.

   He _____ along a path. Then,

suddenly, _____

_____

_____

_____

_____

_____

_____

_____

_____

Unit 5 Commas

The most basic punctuation is that used to demarcate sentences – the capital letter at the beginning and the full stop, exclamation mark or question mark at the end. Once children have grasped this, they can start looking at punctuation that divides up the sentence from within.

The simplest use of commas is to separate items in a list and this unit helps children to use commas in this way. The activities also teach children to take account of commas in reading aloud by pausing momentarily.

Contents

5.1 List likes and dislikes
5.2 Things you recommend at school

5.3 Good things to do
5.4 Things you need – instructions (1)
5.5 Things you need – instructions (2)

Objectives

● Recognise and take account of commas in reading aloud.
● Use commas to separate items in a list.

Ways of teaching

Introduce lists by writing a sentence on the board that uses commas to separate items in a list, for example I *went shopping and bought apples, bananas, grapes and oranges*. Read it aloud. Then read it again, asking the children to notice where you pause as you read. They should be able to tell you that you pause after each of the first two items. Point out the punctuation and tell them that these are commas. They are used to show the reader which are the separate items in the list. They also tell you how to read the sentence. In both ways, they help to make the meaning clear. Explain to the children that you don't need commas between the last two items because they are linked by the word *and*.

Write another similar sentence, this time omitting the commas. Read the sentence aloud and ask the children to tell you where to put the commas. Finally, say a sentence aloud (before writing it), such as In *the pet shop we saw mice, rabbits, fish and hamsters*. Then, as you begin to write it out, ask the children to prompt you on where to put the commas.

During shared reading of a Big Book, ask the children to point out the commas in a list. Invite them to read the sentence aloud, pausing a little at the commas.

In all the activities in this unit, encourage the children to read out their completed sentences, taking account of the commas by pausing slightly. When the children read aloud during guided reading, remind them to notice and use commas in the same way.

About the activities

Activities 5.1 to 5.3

List likes and dislikes, **Things you recommend at school** and **Good things to do**

Ask the children what they like to have for lunch at school – in their packed lunches or school dinners. Write their suggestions in sentences on the board, using commas to separate the items. Point out that there is no comma between the last items linked by *and*. The children may suggest items that are more than one word, such as *cheese sandwiches* or *orange juice*. Demonstrate that the comma comes after the complete item, not after each word, and write an example on the board.

Tell the children that you want them to finish each sentence in activity 5.1 by listing four things for each section. In activity 5.2, the children should imagine that a visitor is coming to their school and they need to tell them the good and bad things about it. In activity 5.3, they make recommendations of things they think people will enjoy doing outside school.

Activities 5.4 and 5.5

Things you need – instructions (1) and **(2)**

These two activities focus on the types of lists that occur in instructional texts. Write the heading *You will need* on the board. Underneath, write a list of ingredients, for example

You will need
eggs
flour
milk

Ask the children where they would see this type of list. Establish that it is a list of recipe ingredients (for pancakes) and show the children some similar lists in a cookery book. Ask the children to help you write another list – for things you need if you go to stay with a friend or relative overnight – *pyjamas*, *toothbrush* and so on. Explain that these lists could be written as sentences and rewrite them together, using commas.

In the activities, the children are asked to decide which list relates to which instruction beginning and to write the items in sentences. Point out that *sun-tan lotion* is one item and remind them that the comma should therefore go after *lotion*.

Following up

Make available some cookery books or books of instructions of how to make or do things. Ask the children to find examples of instructions that include lists (not in sentences) of things 'you will need' and to rewrite them in sentences, using commas to separate the items.

Make a class book about your school, using sentences in which items are separated by commas. Children could list things that are good about the school and those that could be improved or describe the buildings and some of the staff. Alternatively, ask the children to describe their ideal school, listing all of its attributes in sentences. For example, *My ideal school would have a swimming pool, a football pitch, a zoo and a flower garden.*

What I like

Finish these sentences. Then colour over the commas.

For lunch I like _____ ⌐ _____ ⌐

_____ and _____.

For tea I like _____ ⌐ _____ ⌐

_____ and _____.

Some things I **don't** like to eat are

_____ ⌐ _____ ⌐ _____

and _____.

Some people I like are _____ ⌐

_____ ⌐ _____ and

_____.

Some colours I like are _____ ⌐

_____ ⌐ _____ and

_____.

Scholastic Literacy Skills
Grammar and punctuation

▲SCHOLASTIC   photocopiable

My school

Finish these sentences. Use commas to separate
the items in each list. Remember to use **and**.

If you come to my school...

Four helpful people are _____

_____

_____

Four good things we do are _____

_____

_____

_____

Four things you might not like are

_____

_____

_____

Four things to do at playtime are

_____

_____

_____

Four good things

Finish these sentences about what you like to do.
Remember to use commas and the word **and**.

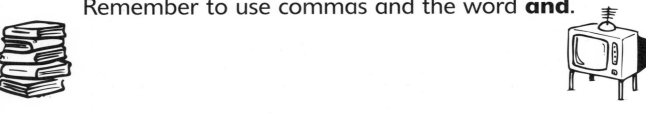

Four funny TV programmes are _____

_____

_____

Four great games are _____

_____

_____

Four fantastic books are _____

_____

_____

Four fun things to do at the weekend are

_____

_____

What you need (1)

Use each of these lists to finish one of the sentences.

a towel	gloves	eggs	lettuce
a bucket	a hat	sugar	cucumber
a spade	a coat	flour	tomatoes
sun-tan lotion	a scarf	butter	celery

To go out in the winter you need

_____, _____,

_____ and _____.

To go to the beach you need

_____, _____,

_____ and _____.

To make a cake you need _____,

_____, _____ and

_____.

To make a salad you need _____,

_____, _____ and

_____.

What you need (2)

Use these lists to finish the sentences.

bread	paper	a cage	glasses
butter	sticky tape	straw	knives
cheese	scissors	food	forks
	ribbon	water	spoons
		a bowl	plates

To wrap a present you need _____

_____

To set the table you need _____

_____

To keep a hamster you need _____

_____

To make a cheese sandwich you need

_____

■SCHOLASTIC photocopiable

Unit 6 Connectives

A connective or conjunction is a word that joins two other words, phrases or sentences. The word *and* is the most common conjunction and one that many children overuse. This unit aims to extend the variety of connectives that children use and make them aware of the differences in meaning that can make their sentences more interesting and varied. For example, *but* implies that something unexpected or disappointing has happened; *then* implies that time has passed between one thing and another; *because* implies a causal relationship between one thing and another.

Contents

6.1 And or *but*? (1)
6.2 And or *but*? (2)
6.3 Use *because*
6.4 Choose between *then* and *because*
6.5 Find the connectives (1)

6.6 Find the connectives (2)
6.7 Link sentences (instructions)
6.8 Link sentences (recount)
6.9 Link sentences to tell a story

Objectives

● Recognise that a variety of words can be used to join sentences.
● Understand how words like *next*, *first* and *then* are used to link sentences and organise text.

Ways of teaching

Explain to the children that you are going to look at a group of words that are used to join sentences together. They are called 'joining words' or connectives. Point out to the children that they probably use *and* a lot in their writing, but there are lots of other words that they could use.

Find a section of a Big Book in which there are a number of connectives, such as *because*, *but*, *after*, *before*, *then* and *so*, and ask the children to help you to look for them. Can they spot which two sentences are being linked? Look at some examples of the children's own writing. Are there places where two sentences could be linked by a joining word? Or can they think of a word to replace *and* as a joining word?

Write some short sentences on pieces of card, such as *We went to the shops. We went to the park.* Use the word *then* to show how they can be linked. Ask the children how they would use the word *after* to join the same two sentences. *After* goes *before* the first sentence or you have to reverse the order of the sentences: *After we went to the shops we went to the park* or *We went to the park after we went to the shops.* It may help to show two pictures to make clear which event happened first. Change the second sentence to *They were closed.* What joining word might they use now? (*But*, because the second sentence is unexpected or disappointing.) Link another two sentences, using *because*, for example *I ate a sandwich. I was hungry.* Spend some time exploring each of these connectives, giving the children pairs of sentences and asking what 'joining word' they would use to link them.

About the activities

Activities 6.1 and 6.2

And or *but*? (1) and (2)

These activities look at the difference in meaning between *and* and *but*. Explain that we use *and* when the outcome is expected (*We went to the park and we played football*). We use *but* when the outcome is disappointing or unexpected (*We went to the park but it rained*).

In activity 6.1, ask the children to join each pair of sentences together using *and* or *but*, rewriting the longer sentence underneath. Remind them that they will not need the full stop at the end of the first sentence, nor the capital letter at the beginning of the second.

The children begin activity 6.2 by completing sentences that are missing suitable connectives – either *and* or *but*. The first two pairs of sentences have the same opening phrases, but the different endings will indicate to the children whether *and* or *but* are required. Advise the children to try out both words each time and see which sounds right in context. Remind them of the occasions when each of these connectives are used, and then encourage them to think of sentences that could be added to the last two sentence starters on the sheet.

Activity 6.3

Use *because*

Talk about joining sentences using *because*. Explain that *because* tells you why something happened. Tell the children that each sentence on the right of the activity sheet can be matched with a sentence on the left. The children may have different suggestions for which sentences go together, but they should join their sentences with *because*, into new, longer sentences. They can then write their own sentence about something they dislike, using *because* to explain why they don't like it. Tell them that they mustn't name any people as the thing disliked.

Activity 6.4

Choose between *then* and *because*

Give the children an opening sentence, for example I *had three pieces of cake*. Then give them two sentences to follow it, one that could be joined with *then* and one that could be joined with *because*, such as I *had a tummy ache* or I *was hungry*. Ask the children to try joining each with *then* and *because*. Which do they think is right? Tell them that they need to work through this process to complete the activity, then use their own words to finish two other sentences that begin with the same phrase.

Activities 6.5 and 6.6

Find the connectives (1) and (2)

Tell the children that each of the sentences in the activities is made up of two shorter sentences linked by a joining word. Activity 6.5 uses *then*, *because*, *but* and *so*; activity 6.6 uses *after*, *because*, *so*, *then* and *before*.

You may like to look at an example of this together. Write a sentence on the board, for example *We had lunch then we went to the cinema*. Explain to the children that one of these words is a joining word, or connective, and if they remove it, they will be left with two sentences. Give a child a piece of card with Blu-Tack and ask the others to tell him or her which word to cover up. When *then* has been covered up, ask what you must do to make what is left into two complete sentences. (Put a full stop after *lunch* and use a capital W for the second *we*.)

Tell the children to find the joining words in the sentences on the sheets. When they have listed the connectives in activity 6.5, encourage them to write their own sentence using one of them. They could then look in books to find more connective words and add them to the list. Draw the children's attention to the connectives in activity 6.6 that give a sense of the timing of events. Help them to think of suitable sentences to follow *before*, *then* and *after*.

Activities 6.7 and 6.8

Link sentences (instructions) and **Link sentences (recounts)**

These activities look at words used to link events in time (*first*, *then*, *next* and so on). They tend to begin sentences and serve to link a sentence to what has gone before, rather than joining two sentences in the way that *and*, *but* and *because* do. (Although the children will have already looked at *after* – a time connective often used in the middle of a sentence.)

Point out opening words like these when you come across them in shared reading and write them up for display. Demonstrate to the children that these words help to put events in order; they give the reader a sense of time passing. They also help the narrative or recount to flow smoothly and so make it easier to read.

Explain to the children that you are going to look for certain words that are often found at the beginning of sentences and that let people know that time is passing. Recap those you have spotted during shared reading, such as *First*, *Then*, *Next*, *Later* and write them on the board. Why do the children think you have started them all with a capital letter? (Because, when used in this way, they begin sentences.)

Move on to talk about what the children do when they get up in the morning – wake up, get out of bed, wash and so on. Note these on the board and tell the children that you want them to write about their morning routine – in the form of instructions and using time connectives.

Looking at activity 6.7, ask the children which word they would start with (*First*) and ask them to complete the three sentences of instructions. Then tell them to use this process to write what the alien should do when he arrives at school in the morning, using pictures as well as sentences to help to make their instructions clear.

Using the sentence openings in activity 6.8, ask the children to write a recount about what they did when they got home from school and then just before going to bed.

Activity 6.9

Link sentences to tell a story

Talk about the words you might use to start sentences in a story. Look at a Big Book together to find words and phrases like *One Day*, *Suddenly*, *At last*, *In the end*… Encourage the children to look out for these phrases in the books they are reading.

This activity aims to encourage the children to use connectives to structure their own writing. Copy the sheet onto card and cut out the words and phrases. The cards can then be used as prompts and inspiration for non-fiction writing as well as stories. If the children are composing fiction, leave out *First* and *Finally*. If they are composing non-fiction, leave out *One day* and *In the end*.

A group of six children should agree on a topic and each take one of the six cards at random. They then decide in which order they are going to speak – beginning with the child who has *One day* (or *First*) and ending with the child who has *In the end* (or *Finally*). The first speaker begins to tell a story (or a recount or instructions) and the others follow in order, each beginning their contribution with the word on his or her card.

Alternatively, several of the cards can be given to one child to structure a piece of fiction or non-fiction writing. Encourage the child to use each of the words or phrases given to begin one sentence in their writing.

Following up
Give groups of children a sentence starter consisting of a short sentence without the final full stop (for example, *We went for a walk*). Then give each pair within the group a different connective (such as, *because*, *but*, *before* and *after*). Let the pairs make up an ending to the sentence that follows on from their connective. The pairs can then share their new, longer sentence with the rest of the class. Compare the new sentences of different pairs within the groups. Talk about how the differ and whether or not each of the endings 'matches' the connective that introduces it.

If children are comfortable with connectives, they could try a similar activity, working independently. Write several sentence starters on strips of card and write a variety of connectives on different coloured pieces of card. Ask individual children to take one starter and one connective and read them out, adding their own ending. So, if one child picks up the starter sentence *We went swimming* and the connective *but*, he might read out, *We went swimming but we forgot our towels*. A second child might pick up the same starter and *after*. She might say, for example, *We went swimming after we saw Dad*.

When reading a shared text, try covering some of the connectives and asking the children to suggest which connective has been covered. Then reveal the orginal and compare it to the children's idea. If the children had suggested a different word, discuss if theirs would work as well as the one in the text and if not, why not.

Ask the children to work with a partner, looking back at some of their written work and identifying places where they have used short sentences. Could they have used connectives to make their writing more interesting? Are there places where they could have used a different connective instead of *and*?

And or but (1)

Join each pair of sentences, using **and** or **but**. Write the new sentences underneath. Remember to change capital letters and use only one full stop for each new sentence.

We went to the shop.   We got some sweets.

_____

It was raining.   We didn't get wet.

_____

I played football.   I didn't get dirty.

_____

Mum made pizza.   I didn't like it.

_____

Go upstairs.   Get your book.

_____

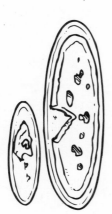

And or but (2)

Complete these sentences by using **and** or **but**.

I went to the park _____ I played football.

I went to the park _____ it rained.

It was my birthday _____ I didn't
have a party.

It was my birthday _____ I
got lots of cards.

It was sunny _____ it was cold.

I wanted an ice cream _____ Dad
got me one.

I got new shoes _____ they didn't fit.

Now finish these sentences in your own words:

I went to the park but _____

_____

I went to school and _____

_____

Scholastic Literacy Skills
Grammar and punctuation

Because...

Each sentence on the left can be joined to one on the right using **because**. Write out the new sentences you make.

I didn't go out.		He fell over.
She laughed	**(because)**	The sun was shining.
He cried.		It was raining.
I was sad.		The dog got muddy.
I was happy.		I lost my teddy.

_____

_____

_____

_____

Finish this sentence:

I don't like _____

because _____

_____

Home

Use these sentences to finish each **We went home...**
Think about which would fit after **then** and **because**.

I was tired.
It was late.   We had tea.
I went to bed.
We made some cakes.
It was getting dark.

We went home then _____

We went home then _____

We went home then _____

We went home because _____

We went home because _____

We went home because _____

Finish these sentences in your own words:

I have breakfast then _____

_____

I have breakfast because _____

_____

Scholastic Literacy Skills
Grammar and punctuation

SCHOLASTIC photocopiable

Joining words

Underline the joining words in these

We had lunch then we went out.

My sister cried because she fell over.

I wanted sweets but Dad said, "No."

It began to rain then the sun came out.

We ran fast but we didn't win the race.

I was tired so I went to bed early.

Write a list of joining words.

_____

_____

_____

_____

Choose one of the words from your list and use it in a sentence.

_____

_____

_____

_____

I saw Leela

Underline the joining words.

I saw Leela after I saw Dan.

My dog hid because she saw a cat.

Emma was ill so she went home.

They had a picnic before they went to the playground.

She had a bath after she played football.

We took off our boots before we went in the house.

Finish these sentences:

I brush my hair before _____

_____

I have tea then _____

_____

I clean my teeth after _____

_____

Instructions for an alien

Complete the instructions below to help an alien to get ready in the morning. Use these phrases:

have breakfast   **get out of bed**   **get dressed**

First _____

Next _____

Then _____

Now use words and pictures to tell the alien what to do when he gets to school. Draw the last picture and write an instruction to go with each picture.

First _____

Next _____

Then _____

After school

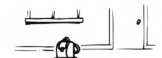

What did you do yesterday when you got home?

First I _____

_____

Next I _____

_____

Then I _____

_____

Later I _____

_____

What did you do at bedtime?

First _____

_____

Next _____

_____

Then _____

_____

Sentence link cards

One day	Suddenly
In the end	Then
Next	First
After a while	Finally

Unit 7 Verbs

Verbs tell us about what is happening. The first aim of this unit is to make children aware of verbs as a part of speech and of the variety of verbs they can use. They go on to think about the notion of time indicated by verbs through their tense. By making explicit the knowledge children already have of things happening in the past, present and future, attention can be drawn to the use of different tenses in their writing, especially the past tense for narrative.

Finally, the unit looks at the agreement between subject and verb.

Contents

Objectives

- Understand what a verb is and what its function is in a sentence.
- Understand the need for grammatical agreement between verbs and nouns/pronouns.
- Use verb tenses correctly.

Ways of teaching

The verb tenses poster offers examples of the way words change when the tense changes. Enlarge the poster and display it in the classroom. During teaching, cover the bold verb in one or other column and ask the children to supply the missing verb in the appropriate tense. Ask the children to suggest other past tense verbs that end in *-ed*. Invite a group of good readers and writers to make their own chart showing examples of other verbs with irregular past tenses.

Remind the children about the groups of words they know about – naming words/nouns; describing words/adjectives. Say that you are going to look at a group of words that tell you what is happening in a sentence, for example *standing, sitting, eating* and explain that these are called *doing words* or *verbs*. Give the children a few examples and then brainstorm as many as you can together. Write the suggestions on the board.

Ask the children to think of verbs that go with particular places, such as at home, on holiday, at school, in the swimming pool. Write these up on separate, large sheets of paper for display.

For homework, ask the children to list verbs that describe what they do after school and through the evening – *eating, playing, washing* and so on.

When you come to look at verb tenses, ask the children what they are doing now, encouraging them to answer in sentences (for example, I *am listening. I am looking at the book.*). Explain that these things are happening in the *present*. Ask them to tell you what they did yesterday (*looked, listened* and so on) and what they will do tomorrow. Don't worry at this stage about different forms of the tense, for example I *am sitting* or I *sit*.

About the activities

Activity 7.1   **Using verbs (1)**

Tell the children some of the things you can do – *walk, skate, drive, play the piano* and so on, then ask them to tell you some of the things they can do. Ask them to write on the activity sheet four of the things they can do. Explain that they can use the words given or think of their own. They should then finish the sentences about birds and dogs, and finally think of another group of creatures (real or imaginary) and say what those creatures can do. (For example, *Fish can… Dragons can…*)

Activity 7.2   **Using verbs (2)**

This activity uses a specific form of verb – the present participle. If the children ask about it, explain that a verb ending changes depending on the sort of sentence the verb is in. The children will probably know which ending to use because it will sound right. Point out that, in this activity, all the verbs end in *-ing*.

Ask the children to list verbs to state what they like and don't like doing. There are suggested verbs given, but you may like to brainstorm others with the children.

Activity 7.3   **Using verbs (3)**

You can prepare for this activity by sharing a large illustration of an imaginary character (possibly from a story the children have read). Ask the children to imagine what the character might do if she or her were angry, for example *shout* or *bellow*. What about if he were sad?

Ask them to create their own monster and write about him, using the sentence starters in the activity.

Activity 7.4   **Verb variety (*said*)**

Explain to the children that there are lots of different verbs that can be used to describe the same thing – but they all have a slightly different meaning and create different effects. In shared reading, ask the children to spot words that are used instead of *said*.

Read out the story of 'Little Red Riding Hood' on the sheet, inserting the word *said* in each of the gaps. Help the children to appreciate that the story could be much more interesting if the author had sometimes used words other than *said*. Tell the children to rewrite the story, filling all the gaps with interesting verbs. There is a selection given at the bottom of the page, but the children may be able to think of their own. Afterwards, compare different versions and talk about the effects.

Activities 7.5 and 7.6   **Past tense (*-ed*) and Past tense (irregular endings)**

During shared reading of a story (or referring to the story in activity 7.4), point out to the children that the story is told as if the events have already happened. They happened in the *past*. Read a section of your chosen text, changing the verbs into the present tense, and ask children to tell you how this changes the story.

Now write the first few sentences of a story in the present tense and ask the children to help you change it into the past. You can make up the story or use the beginning of a published text. In the latter case, compare the class's rewritten version with the original.

Ask the children to change the sentences in the activities from present to past tense, imagining that everything happened yesterday. Encourage the children to re-read their writing, checking for consistent use of tenses, and draw attention to the -ed endings in activity 7.5.

In shared writing, demonstrate how to edit or make corrections.

Activity 7.7

Present and past

Ask the children to tell you about some of the things that they did when they were little. Encourage them to give their answers in sentences in the simple past tense, such as I *crawled*. Ask them if they still do those things and, if not, what they do instead, for example I *walk* or I *run*. Read through the activity sheet, explaining to the children that they should write about themselves now, and compare each situation to what they would have done when they were little.

Activity 7.8

Tell a story in the past tense

Remind the children that stories are usually told in the past tense – as if things happened a long time ago. Together, briefly retell the story of 'Jack and the Beanstalk' then explain that the beginning of that story is on the sheet. All the 'doing words' are in the present tense and the children need to write the past tense forms in the gaps. When they have finished, ask them to think about what happened next and to write the rest of the story, continuing in the past tense.

When they are writing their own stories, remind the children to use the past tense. Encourage them to re-read their writing, checking they have been consistent in their use of tenses.

Activities 7.9 and 7.10

Subject agreement (1) and **(2)**

Write a simple sentence on the board, for example B*obby likes chocolate*. Rub out B*obby* and put in I instead. Read the new version out and ask the children if it still sounds right. They should be able to tell you that the word *likes* sounds wrong. By telling them that sometimes the verb changes according to who is 'doing' the action, you will be making explicit knowledge they already have and use orally.

Write another simple sentence, such as *Raj and Sam want pudding*. Ask the children to tell you which is the verb, then rub out *Raj and Sam* and put in We. Ask if the verb changes this time. Change W*e* to H*e* and invite the children to say if the sentence is correct. What is wrong with it and how should they change it?

In the activities, suggest to the children that they say both words from each gap out loud to see which sounds right before writing one on the line.

At the bottom of activity 7.9, explain that they should write a sentence in the *present* tense about what sort of thing they usually do after school. In 7.10, they should write similar sentences about what they and their friends get up to on Saturdays.

Following up

During a shared reading session using a Big Book, ask the children to tell you which is the verb in each sentence as you read. Can they suggest some alternatives that would fit in the sentence? Then ask the children to take a piece of their own writing and underline the verbs, thinking of others that they could have used instead.

In pairs, the children could look through books for words that have been used instead of *said* and *went*. They can then try to come up with some of their own. Ask them to look through some of their writing and see if there are places where some of these words could have been used. Tell them to replace a few and read the old and then the new sentence out loud. What effect does the new word have?

Play a game of charades, asking a child to mime a verb while the other children try to guess what it is.

When you are writing out lists of the tasks the children are going to be working through, ask the children to point out the verb each time, for example *Finish, Write, Copy*.

Go around school on a verb hunt, asking the children to look out for verbs in displays, notices and signs.

Give the children a sentence starter, for example I *went out with my friend and we*… Then go around the class, asking each child to say the phrase and add on a verb in the past tense that begins with the next letter of the alphabet. Explain to the children that they may need to add a noun as well for the sentence to make sense, for example I *went out with my friend and we acted. I went out with my friend and we bought boats.*

What can you do?

What can you do? Use the words in the box,
or your own, to finish these sentences:

I can _____

I can _____

I can _____

I can _____

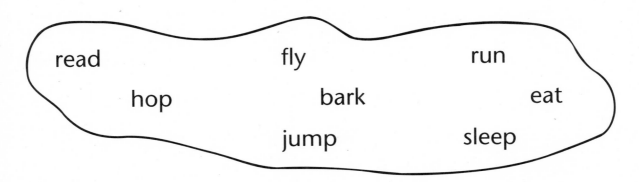

read   fly   run

hop   bark   eat

jump   sleep

Birds can _____

Dogs can _____

Think of another type of animal. What can they do?

_____ can _____

What I like doing

Write lists of things you like doing and things you don't like doing. You can use some of the words below.

I like   I don't like

_____   _____

_____   _____

_____   _____

_____   _____

_____   _____

helping	camping	dancing
talking	singing	washing
skipping	running	swimming
tidying	reading	playing

I am good at _____

I want to get better at _____

My monster

Draw a monster. Finish the sentences by saying
what he likes to do.

When my monster is cross he likes to

_____

When he is happy he likes to _____

When he is sad he likes to _____

In school, he likes to _____

At home, he likes to _____

In the park, he likes to _____

Best of all, he likes to _____

Little Red Riding Hood

Fill in the gaps in this story by using more interesting words than **said**. There are some words at the bottom of the page to help you.

"Hello, little girl," ___growled___ the wolf.

Little Red Riding Hood felt scared. "Hello Mr Wolf," she _____.

"Where are you going?" _____ the wolf.

"To visit my grandma," _____ Little Red Riding Hood.

"Can I come with you?" the wolf _____.

"No!" _____ Little Red Riding Hood, and she ran away as fast as she could.

shouted	called	whispered	growled
asked	answered	yelled	hissed	muttered

Yesterday

Rewrite these sentences so the events happened in the past.

I walk to school.
Yesterday, _____

They laugh at the clown.
Yesterday, _____

Sammy picks strawberries.
Yesterday, _____

She jumps up and down.
Yesterday, _____

We talk to the teacher.
Yesterday, _____

I dance in my bedroom.
Yesterday, _____

What did you do yesterday?

_____

_____

In the past

Rewrite these sentences so the
events happened in the past.

They go shopping.
Yesterday, they _____

I have a bath.
Last night, _____

Mum takes the dog for a walk.
Yesterday, _____

We swim in the big pool.
Last Saturday, _____

I sing a new song.
Last week, _____

What did you see on your way to school?_____

_____

What did you eat last night?_____

_____

When I was little

Write about yourself now.
Then write similar sentences
about yourself in the past.

Now I am _____

When I was little I was _____

Now I like _____

When I was little I _____

Now I eat _____

When I was little I _____

Now I wear _____

When I was little I _____

Now I _____

When I was little I _____

Jack and the Beanstalk

Write the story as if it happened a long time ago,
changing the verbs to fit the gaps.

Jack and his mother _____ poor, but
are

they _____ a cow. Jack _____
have goes

to market and he _____ it. Then he
sells

_____ home.
walks

He _____ his mother what he
shows

_____ for the cow.
gets

"Beans!" she _____. "That's no
shouts

good!" She _____ so angry that she
is

_____ the beans out of the window.
throws

Next morning, Jack _____ out
looks

of the window.

Like or likes?

Finish these sentences by choosing the right verb each time.

I _____ school.

    like / likes

Pat _____ hard.

    work / works

They _____ off the box.

    jump / jumps

Dad _____ at home time.

    come / comes

I _____ on the floor.

    sit / sits

They _____ to school by bus.

    come / comes

Mum _____ the trumpet.

    play / plays

Now finish this sentence. Choose your verb carefully.

After school I usually _____

_____

Saturdays

Choose the right word to fill each gap.

On Saturday mornings my dad _____

take / takes

me to the park. My friend Pete _____

go / goes

too. We _____ football. Then he

play / plays

_____ to my house and we

come / comes

_____ lunch. If it is raining, I

have / has

_____ at home. I _____

stay / stays   play / plays

on the computer or I _____ a book.

read / reads

What do you do on a Saturday morning?_____

_____

What does your friend do?_____

_____

Unit 8 Adjectives

Adjectives describe nouns – they tell us something about a person, place, feeling and so on. Children can have lots of fun exploring them orally through word games. Encourage them to use their imaginations – describing what they see in their mind's eye and trying to enable others to see it; describing a simple noun so that it seems funny, scary, wicked and so on. They will learn that by using adjectives imaginatively, they will make their writing more interesting and help their reader to picture what they are writing about.

Contents

8.1 Describe a noun
8.2 Describe yourself
8.3 Describe a cat and a baby
8.4 Find synonyms for *big, little, kind* and *unkind*

8.5 Use adjectives for interest
8.6 Make an advert persuasive
8.7 Colour adjectives
8.8 Make the story more interesting
8.9 Describe the person

Objectives

- Understand that adjectives evoke things more vividly and make text more interesting.
- Use adjectives in their own writing.
- Increase their vocabulary of adjectives.

Ways of teaching

Although the children do not need to use the term *adjective*, they should begin to discover the function and explore the variety of adjectives.

Write a simple sentence on the board, for example I *have a cat*. Ask the children what they know about your cat from that sentence. Does it tell them what it looks like or how it behaves? Add an adjective, such as *fluffy* and ask them if that helps and why. Now ask the children to imagine that each of them has a cat. Tell them that not all cats are the same and you want them to think of a word to describe their cat. Invite them to add their word to the sentence, for example I *have a friendly cat*. I *have a crazy cat*. Write their words on the board and tell them that these are adjectives or describing words. Repeat the process with other nouns, such as *flower* or *car*.

About the activities

Activity 8.1

Describe a noun
Remind the children what they know about describing words. Hold up a classroom object, such as a book, and ask the children to suggest words to describe it. If they say *red*, take the opportunity to point out that colour words are describing words too. Now ask the children to look at the objects in the activity and to think of suitable describing words. They should also draw their own object and describe it, using an adjective and noun.

Activity 8.2

Describe yourself
Tell the children that they are going to explore words to describe themselves. You may like to prepare for this by using the sheet as a model to describe you and inviting the children's help to complete the activity. Talk through the words at the bottom of the sheet to ensure understanding.

Activity 8.3

Describe a cat and a baby

Ask the children if all dogs, babies, cats or houses are the same. Write the word *house* on the board and ask the children to suggest different words to describe a house, for example *old, enormous, dirty*. Write these words in a web around *house*. Ask a child to make a sentence about a house using two of the adjectives, for example *The house is enormous and dirty*. Ask the other children to shut their eyes and imagine the house. Invite other children to describe a different house for the rest of the class to try to 'see' in their minds.

Using the activity sheet, ask the children to think of as many words as they can to describe cats and babies. They should then go on to draw a picture and write a short sentence about one of each, using two describing words in each sentence.

Activity 8.4

Find synonyms for *big*, *little*, *kind* and *unkind*

Tell the children that there are lots of describing words that we could use and it is a pity to use one or two over and over again. Compare two items of different sizes, such as a pencil and a table. Which is big and which is little? Now compare the pencil with something very small – a crumb or a tiny scrap of paper. If the pencil is *little*, can the children think of a word to describe the crumb? Help them to think of a variety of adjectives.

Emphasise to the children that their writing will be more interesting if they use a variety of describing words. Ask them to work in pairs to think of three different words for each of the adjectives on the sheet.

Activity 8.5

Use adjectives for interest

Read the following story to the children:

> One day, a monster invited me for tea. We had soup, pizza and pudding. Then I looked around the monster's house. It had a kitchen, two bedrooms and a garden. I stayed the night. Next morning, I went home.

Help the children to see that describing words would have made the story more interesting and tell them that they have the chance to put some in on the activity sheet. They could work in pairs and discuss whether it was a good experience (with hot, tasty soup and a soft bed) or a scary experience and should try to think of appropriate adjectives while they are talking. As they complete the sheet, encourage them to use two adjectives now and again if they can, for example *The garden was dark and gloomy*.

You could go on to ask the children what more they would have liked to know and note their suggestions. (What did the monster say? Did anything strange happen in the night?) These ideas can be explored later in a shared writing session.

Activity 8.6

Make an advert persuasive

Lead up to this activity by looking at some published advertisements aimed at children. What sort of words do they use? Ask the children to bring in some comics and magazines so that you can look at the adverts together. Write up some of the adjectives used.

Read through the 'Choc Chews' advert and ask the children what they think of it. Do the sweets sound exciting? Why not? Read out the words at the bottom of the page and then ask the children to use some of them (and some of their own) to make the advert more appealing.

When the children have completed the activity, ask one child to read out the original advert, then ask another child to read out his or her rewritten one. Which one would encourage the children to buy the sweets? Ask the children to write a sentence or two about sweets that they like, again, using exciting and persuasive adjectives.

Activity 8.7

Colour adjectives

Put a selection of objects on a table, making sure there are different numbers of items in various colours, for example three pencils (one red, two green), two rubbers, a blue cup. Ask the children to describe what is there. They may begin by saying *Some pencils, two rubbers and a cup*, so, encourage them to use colour and number words. Tell them that these are describing words too.

Tell the children that you want them to colour in the picture in the activity and then describe it. Remind them to use colour and number words as they did during the whole-class work.

Activity 8.8

Make the story more interesting

Read out the story starter at the top of the sheet. Ask the children if they think it could be made more interesting and how. Ask them to improve the story by adding words from the boxes to tell us more about the characters. Point out the commas that separate the items in a list.

The children can then go on to write more of the story. Help them to understand that the adjectives they have used will decide what sort of story this is. If the dragon is friendly, it will be a different story than if it is fierce. And if the boy is enormous and strong it may be different than if he were skinny and feeble.

Activity 8.9

Describe the person

You could introduce this activity by working through a shared version of it first. Display a photograph of someone from a magazine and ask the children to suggest adjectives to describe him or her. List their suggestions on the board. Then ask the children to make up some sentences about the person, using adjectives from the list. Encourage them to think of a variety of sentence types – they might use conjunctions to make more complex sentences, for example H*e is tired because he has walked a long way*.

Now ask the children to cut a picture of their own from a magazine and to work through the process you have practised together to complete the sheet.

Following up

Look back at familiar characters from stories and invite the children to say why they liked or disliked them. For example, I *like Snow White because she's kind. I don't like the queen because she's wicked.*

Choose a noun, such as *friend*, and go around the class, asking the children to think of a word beginning with the next letter of the alphabet to describe an imaginary friend. For example, *My friend is angry… bossy… cute…* You may have to help out with some letters and explain that not all the adjectives need to be positive (nor all negative). Alternately, choose one letter of the alphabet and try to find as many adjectives as you can to describe a noun, for example *My dog is mean… messy… minute…*

What's it like?

Add a word to describe each of these:

the _____ face

the _____ man

the _____ plate

the _____ baby

the _____ dog

the _____ monster

the _____ day

Draw something and describe it.

the _____

All about me

What are you like? Use adjectives to describe yourself.
You can use some of the words from the bottom of the page.

My hair is _____ and _____

My eyes are _____ and _____

My face is _____ and _____

My hands are _____ and

_____

My feet are _____ and _____

Sometimes I am _____ and

_____

Sometimes I am _____ and

_____

curly	straight	short	long
square	round	long	wide
big thin	small	happy	miserable
cross	funny	kind	rude

Cats and babies

What words could you use to describe cats?
What about babies? Write as many as you can
think of around the pictures.

Draw a cat and a baby. Finish the sentences about them.

The baby is _____ and _____

The cat is _____ and _____

Mr and Mrs Giant

Think of three words that mean the same as each one in bold.

The giant is **big**.

_____

_____

_____

His wife is **little**.

_____

_____

_____

He is **unkind**.

_____

_____

_____

She is **kind**.

_____

_____

Tea with a monster

Finish this story by adding really interesting adjectives.

A monster invited me for tea.

The soup was _____

The pizza was _____

The pudding was _____

I looked round the monster's house.

The kitchen was _____

The spare bedroom was _____

The garden was _____

I stayed the night.

The bed was _____

Next morning, I felt _____

Choc Chews

Rewrite this advert, using words that are more exciting than **nice**. Some words are given below to help you.

Buy these **nice** sweets.
They taste **nice**.
They are **nice**.
Choc Chews make you feel **nice**.
Get some now!

Buy these _____ sweets.
They taste _____
They are _____
Choc Chews make you feel _____
Get some now!

fantastic	amazing	enormous	giant
brilliant	wicked	great	sad
wonderful	delicious	scrummy	yummy

Use the back of this sheet to write about your favourite sweets.

On the beach

Colour in the picture. Then write about it, using colour and number words.

_____

_____

_____

_____

_____

_____

_____

Droogal the dragon

This is the beginning of a story. Can you make it more interesting by adding some of the words from the smoke?

Droogal was a dragon. He lived in a castle. He had teeth, eyes and claws.

One day, Droogal saw a boy coming to his castle. The boy had arms, legs and eyes. He had a dog.

Droogal was a _____ dragon. He lived in a _____ castle. He had _____ teeth, _____ eyes and _____ claws.

pointed   spikey   blobby   friendly   soppy   blue   terrible   pretty   powerful   perfect

One day Droogal saw a _____ boy coming to his castle. The boy had _____ arms, _____ legs and _____ eyes. He had a _____ dog.

tiny   massive   weak   flashing   crazy   gentle   skinny   funny   fierce   kind

Describe someone

Stick a photograph of someone here.
List words that describe him or her.

Write two sentences about your person,
using some of the describing words from your list.

Unit 9 Speech

This unit helps children to differentiate between spoken and unspoken words in a sentence. Children are asked to focus on the words people say, before looking at the function of speech bubbles. Attention is then drawn to speech marks and how they separate speech from the rest of the sentence. At this stage, children are not asked to use speech marks, only to be aware of their function.

Contents

9.1 What do people say?
9.2 What are people saying?
9.3 What are people answering?

9.4 What would you say?
9.5 Which words are spoken?
9.6 Peace and quiet

Objectives

- Investigate the use of speech bubbles.
- Recognise that spoken words are marked off from the rest of a sentence.
- Identify speech marks and understand their function.

Ways of teaching

Poster 3 picks out, from within sentences, the words that people say. Point out to the children that the spoken words are those inside the speech marks. Cover the speech bubbles and ask the children to tell you which words each person says. Use the examples to show that spoken words can come before or after the name of the person who speaks. Try changing the order, for example *'I'm going out,' said* Dad.

Show the children some examples of speech bubbles, in Big Books if possible, or in comics. Ask if they know why the words are in bubbles. They will probably be able to tell you that these are the words people say. Display several photographs or magazine illustrations of people and attach a large paper speech bubble to each person. Ask the children to suggest what each person might be saying. Agree some words for the first and write them in his or her bubble. Draw attention to the fact that you don't write *he said* or *she shouted*, only the spoken words. Do the same for the other people, asking the children to prompt you on which words to write in the bubbles.

In a later session, look at a Big Book that has direct speech. Point out the speech marks and explain that these are used to show us which words are spoken. Show the children that they are placed before the first spoken word and after the last one. Ask the children to help you find the spoken words on the Big Book page. One child could come out and underline a character's words lightly in coloured chalk; another could circle the speech marks.

About the activities

Activity 9.1

What do people say?

Talk about the sorts of things people usually say to the children. Ask them to tell you what you say when they are making a noise, at lunchtime and so on. On the board, draw a stick figure of yourself with speech bubbles. Write some of the phrases the children quote in these bubbles, asking them to tell you exactly which words to write. Ask them to think of what people at home say – their mum, dad, carer, older brother and so on – when certain things happen.

Read through the activity with the children and tell them to write just the words people say in the bubbles. When they have finished, ask them to use the back of the sheet to draw another event happening at home and what someone involved says. Encourage the children to read out what they have written, using appropriate intonation and expression.

Activity 9.2 **What are people saying?**
This time, the children should look at each illustration in the activity and imagine they are in the situation. What would they say? They should then write the words each child says in the appropriate bubble.On the back of the sheet, they could draw themselves with a friend and write their conversation in speech bubbles. Ask the children to read out their work with expression.

Activity 9.3 **What are people answering?**
Show the children that there are five situations in the activity and in each case, there are two children. The children should read the words spoken by the child on the left and decide what the child on the right might reply, writing the words in the speech bubble.

Activity 9.4 **What would you say?**
Read the verse by Spike Milligan and ask the children to tell you which words the king says. Point out that they have been written in his speech bubble. The children should then do the same exercise for the cat's words.

For the remaining three verses, the children should make up the rest of the spoken words, then transfer them to the bubbles. You may want to complete the mouse's verse as a shared activity to demonstrate what they are to do. The mouse might repeat 'Look at…' or it might say something else. Ask the children for suggestions and write them on the board. For example, 'Clean my house.' or 'Come into my house.' The children could then write more verses for this poem, using If I were a boy/gran/fish and so on.

Activity 9.5 **Which words are spoken?**
Ask the children to remind you what happens in 'Goldilocks and the Three Bears'. Tell them that they are going to look at part of that story and find what the characters say. Read the extract on the sheet and ask the children to read it again to themselves, looking for the words that the bears speak. Advise them to shade over them with a coloured pencil. They should then use the illustration of Baby Bear to write some speech for him.

Activity 9.6 **Peace and quiet**
Explain to the children that Mrs Dray is a busy squirrel with a young family whose demands take up a lot of her time. Today, she wants some time to herself. Read the extract together before asking the children to re-read it to themselves, looking for the words that the squirrels speak. Tell them to shade the spoken words lightly with a coloured pencil.

They can then read it aloud in pairs, talking about how the squirrels might have said the words. Help them to imagine what might have happened next and what was said. Tell them to draw two of the characters and write their conversation in speech bubbles.

Following up In shared reading, focus on an extract from a familiar story which has plenty of dialogue. Read the extract, telling the children to look for the words that the characters speak. Invite children to come out and lightly underline the spoken words. You could then ask two children to take on the roles of the characters and act out the conversation, each saying only the words that his or her character says. The children could go on to draw one of the characters and write some of his or her spoken words in speech bubbles.

At home

What do people at home say when these things happen?

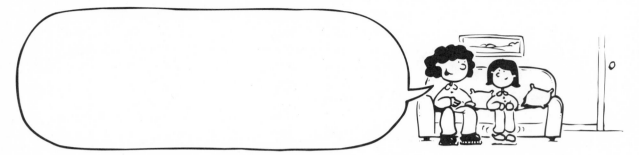

You don't want to go to bed.

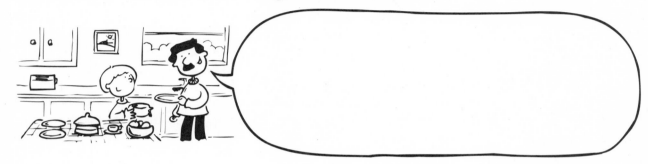

You help tidy up.

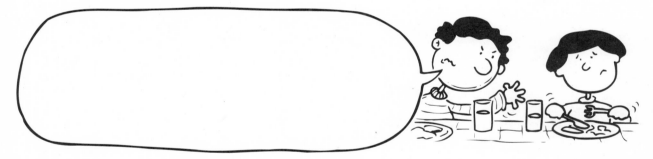

You don't like the food.

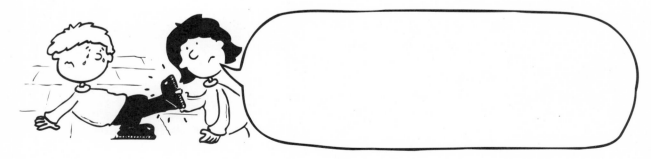

You hurt yourself.

What are they saying?

What do you think these children are saying?
Write their words in the speech bubbles.

Write the answers

Read what each child says.
What do you think the other child answers?

Oh no!

I can't find my shoe.

I like chocolate.

It's mine!

Why are you crying?

If I were a king...

Read the first two verses. Then complete the others.

If I were a king
I'd say,
"Kiss my ring."

Spike Milligan

Kiss my ring.

If I were a cat
I'd say,
"Look at my hat."

If I were a mouse
I'd say,
"_____ my house."

If I were a star
I'd say,
"_____ my car."

If I were a cook
I'd say,
"_____ my book."

The Three Bears

Lightly shade the words that the bears say.

The Three Bears came home. They went into the sitting room. Father Bear said, "Who's been sitting in my chair?"

Mother Bear said, "Who's been sitting in my chair?"

Baby Bear said, "Who's been sitting in my chair and has broken it?"

Then the Three Bears went into the kitchen. Father Bear said, "Who's been eating my porridge?"

Mother Bear said, "Who's been eating my porridge?"

What do you think Baby Bear said?

Suzie and the spider

Shade the words that are spoken.

"What are you doing, Suzie?" asked Mrs Dray.

"I'm watching that spider," said Suzie, smiling.

"Spider! Where?" Her mum gasped.

"It's gone under the table," replied Suzie.

"I can't see it any more."

Mrs Dray didn't like spiders, but was *not* going to look for it now. She looked at Suzie and said, "You're meant to be helping Dad look after the baby."

"Yes," muttered Suzie. But she didn't move.

"*Off* you go, then," Mrs Dray said. "I'm going to sit here quietly. And I don't want to be disturbed."

What do you think happened next? Did the spider come back? What did Mum say? What about Dad?

Links to the National Literacy Strategy Framework for Teaching – word-level objectives for Reception and sentence-level objectives for Year 1

		Unit 1	Unit 2	Unit 3	Unit 4	Unit 5	Unit 6	Unit 7
R	W3	1–4						
Y1/Term 1	S9		1, 2		1–6			3
	S8		1–7					
	S7		3–7		7–11	1–5		
	S6		3–7	1–4	1–5, 9–17	4, 5		
	S5		1–7		1–6	4, 5		
	S4						1–8	
	S3						1–8	
	S2						1–8	
	S1					4, 5	1–8	3
Y1/Term 2	S7		1, 2, 5–7		1–17			3–5
	S6		2–7	1–4		4		4
	S5							
	S4		1–7		1–6	4, 5		
	S3					4, 5	1–8	
	S2					4, 5		
	S1			1–4	1–6	4, 5	1–8	4
Y1/Term 3	S7		8–11	4–6	7–17	7–17		3–8
	S6			4				
	S5					1–6		
	S4							
	S3		8–10		1–6	1		
	S2				1	4, 5		
	S1				1–6	4, 5		

Links to the National Literacy Strategy Framework for Teaching – sentence-level objectives for Year 2

		Unit 1	Unit 2	Unit 3	Unit 4	Unit 5	Unit 6	Unit 7	Unit 8	Unit 9
Y2/Term 1	S1				1–4					
	S2									
	S3	10, 11		7, 8						
	S4	1, 4								
	S5		1–6				1–9			
Y2/Term 2	S1	1–10, 12			1–4	1–5				4–6
	S2	10, 12								
	S3	10, 12		7, 8	2–4					
	S4									
	S5		1–6					5, 6, 8		
	S6							5–8		4–6
	S7							9, 10		1–3
	S8					1–5				
	S9					1–5				
Y2/Term 3	S1		1–6		1–4					
	S2				2, 3			9, 10		
	S3	10, 12						1–8		
	S4	1, 4				1–5				1–3
	S5					1–5				
	S6	1–12		1–10						
	S7			9, 10						
	S8									
	S9									

(Sentence-level work on adjectives is not detailed in the NLS at Year 2)

Links to *Curriculum and Assessment in Scotland* – National Guidelines for English Language 5–14

Unit	Skill focus	Attainment Outcomes, Targets and Levels		
		Reading	Writing: Punctuation and structure	Writing: Knowledge about language
Ages 5-6				
1	Lower case and capital letters	A	–	–
2	Capital letters, full stops and question marks	A	A	–
3	Is it a sentence?	A	A	–
4	Sentences make sense	A	–	A
5	Signs and sentences	A	–	A
6	Grammatical awareness	A	–	A
7	Common and proper nouns	B	–	B
Ages 6-7				
1	Sentences	B	B	–
2	Proper nouns	B/C	–	B/C
3	Questions	B	B	–
4	Grammatical awareness	A	–	A
5	Commas	B	B	–
6	Connectives	B	B	–
7	Verbs	–	–	B/C
8	Adjectives	–	–	B/C
9	Speech	C/D	C/D	–